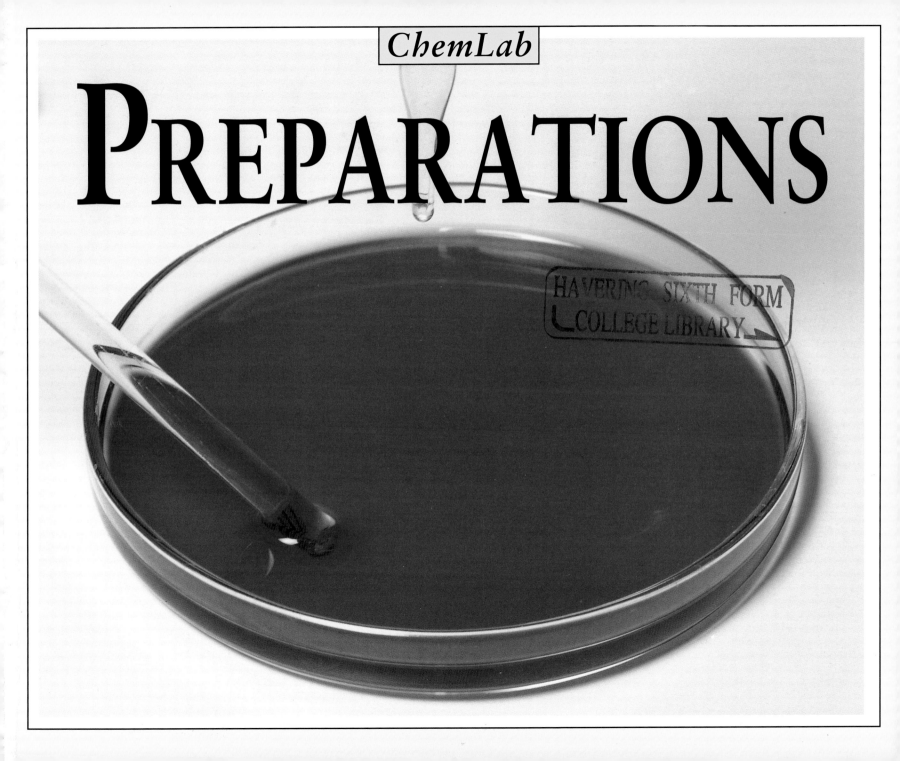

ChemLab

PREPARATIONS

Atlantic Europe Publishing

First published in 1998 by Atlantic Europe Publishing
Company Limited, Greys Court Farm, Greys Court,
Henley-on-Thames, Oxon, RG9 4PG, UK.

Copyright © 1998
Atlantic Europe Publishing Company Limited

Author
Brian Knapp, BSc, PhD
Project consultant
*Keith B. Walshaw, MA, BSc, DPhil
(Head of Chemistry, Leighton Park
School)*
Project Director
Duncan McCrae, BSc
Editor
Mary Sanders, BSc
Special photography
Ian Gledhill
**Electronic page make-up
and illustrations**
The Ascenders Partnership
Designed and produced by
EARTHSCAPE EDITIONS
Print consultants
Chromo Litho Ltd
Reproduced in Malaysia by
Global Colour
Printed and bound in Italy by
L.E.G.O. SpA

Suggested cataloguing location
Knapp, Brian
Preparations
ISBN 1 869860 72 1
– ChemLab series, volume 11
540

Picture credits
All photographs are from the **Earthscape
Editions** photolibrary except the
following:
(c=centre t=top b=bottom l=left r=right)
Mary Evans Picture Library 7t

*This product is manufactured from sustainable
managed forests. For every tree cut down at
least one more is planted.*

Contents

HOW TO USE THIS BOOK

These two pages show you how to get the most from this book.

❶ THE CONTENTS

Use the table of contents to see how this book is divided into themes. Each theme may have one or more demonstrations.

❷ THEMES

Each theme begins with a theory section on yellow-coloured paper. Major themes may contain several pages of theory for the demonstrations that are presented on the subsequent pages. They also contain biographies of scientists, whose work was important in the understanding of the theme.

❸ DEMONSTRATIONS

Demonstrations are at the heart of any chemistry study. However, many demonstrations cannot easily be shown to a whole class for health and safety reasons, because the demonstration requires a close-up view, because it is over too quickly, takes too long to complete, or because it requires special apparatus. The demonstrations shown here have been photographed especially to overcome these problems and give you a very close-up view of the key stages in each reaction.

The text, pictures and diagrams are closely connected. To get the best from the demonstration, look closely at each picture as soon as its reference occurs in the text.

Many of the pictures show enlarged views of parts of the demonstration to help you see exactly what is happening. Notice, too, that most pictures form part of a sequence. You will find that it pays to look at the picture sequence more than once, and always be careful to make sure you can see exactly what is described in any picture before you move on.

The main heading for a demonstration or a set of demonstrations.

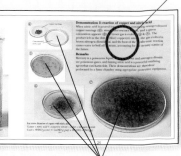

An introduction expands on the heading, summarising the demonstration or group of demonstrations and their context in the theme.

Each demonstration is carefully explained and illustrated with photographs and, where necessary, with diagrams, tables and graphs. The illustrations referred to are numbered ①, ②, ③, etc.

Chemical equations are shown where appropriate (see the explanation of equations at the bottom of page 5).

The photographs show the key stages that you might see if you witness a demonstration at first-hand. Examine them very carefully against the text description.

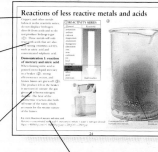

APPARATUS

The demonstrations have been carefully conducted as representative examples of the main chemical processes. The apparatus used is standard, but other choices are possible and you may see different equipment in your laboratory, so make sure you understand the principles behind the apparatus selected. The key pieces of apparatus are defined in the glossary.

❹ GLOSSARY OF TECHNICAL TERMS

Words with which you may be unfamiliar are shown in small capitals where they first occur in the text. Use the glossary on pages 66–74 to find more information about these technical words. Over 400 items are presented alphabetically.

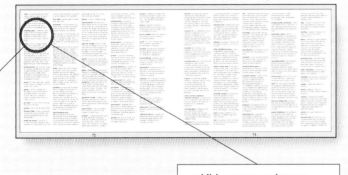

❺ INDEX TO ALL VOLUMES IN THE SET

To look for key words in any of the 12 volumes that make up the ChemLab set, use the Master Index on pages 75 to 80. The instructions on page 75 show you how to cross-reference between volumes.

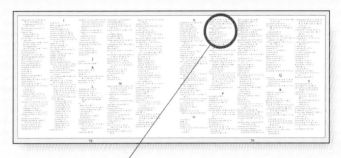

The most important locations of the term 'oxidising agent' are given in a master index which includes references to all of the volumes in the ChemLab set.

oxidising agent: a substance that removes electrons from another substance being oxidised (and therefore is itself reduced) in a redox reaction. *Example:* chlorine (Cl_2).

ABBREVIATIONS

Units are in the international metric system. Some units of measurement are abbreviated, or shortened, as follows:
°C = degrees Celsius
km = kilometre
m = metre
cm = centimetre
mm = millimetre
sq m = square metre
g = gram
kg = kilogram
kJ = kilojoule
l = litre

❻ CHEMICAL EQUATIONS

Important or relevant chemical equations are shown in written and symbolic form together with additional information.

What the reaction equation illustrates

Where relevant, the oxidation state is shown as Roman numerals in brackets.

The symbol indicating the state of each substance is shown as follows:
(s) = solid
(g) = gaseous
(l) = liquid
(aq) = aqueous
($conc$) = concentrated

Word equation

Symbol equation
The symbols for each element can be found in any Periodic Table.

EQUATION: Reaction of copper and nitric acid

$Copper + nitric\ acid \rightarrow copper(II)\ nitrate + water + nitrogen\ dioxide$

$Cu(s) + 4HNO_3(conc) \rightarrow Cu(NO_3)_2(aq) + 2H_2O(l) + 2NO_2(g)$

Blue

The two halves of the chemical equation are separated by the arrow that shows the progression of the reaction. Each side of the equation must balance.

Sometimes additional descriptions are given below the symbol equation.

The correct number of atoms, ions and molecules and their proportions in any compound are shown by the numbers. A free electron is shown as an e^-.

5

INTRODUCTION

Chemistry is essentially a practical subject, undertaken largely by experiments in a chemistry laboratory. Over the centuries, the careful work of scientists has built up a vast store of knowledge about how to work successfully and safely with chemicals. The methods used are known as standard techniques. Of course, such techniques and preparations were only developed through considerable experimentation down the centuries. Many of the techniques and preparations described here are therefore the classic demonstrations of their kind.

Although you will find some substances (known as REAGENTS) in bottles, ready for use, on a chemistry laboratory shelf, there are many others that have to be prepared before further experiments can be undertaken. Again, long experience has shown that there are certain standard ways of preparation, many designed to make the most economical use of materials (REACTANTS) that are easily available.

How techniques and preparations were developed

Even in ancient times, the useful properties of some substances were exploited. The techniques developed by the early technicians were the result of trial and error. Preparations such as REFINING metals, DISTILLING SOLUTIONS to make alcohol, and ACIDS, or making gunpowder, worked well enough for everyday purposes, but the chemistry of the substances in use was not known.

However, by the 16th century, the new Renaissance period had produced a spirit of enquiry and, with it, the first academic scientists, who sought to describe and explain the way materials behaved. Moreover, they published what they found, so that knowledge could be shared and rapidly built upon.

These pioneer scientists were usually wealthy people who had the time and resources to experiment however they chose. It was soon realised that many of the substances produced by different methods were, in fact, chemically the same; there were a limited number of pure substances, each of which had distinctive properties.

One of the earliest experimental scientists of this period was the Belgian chemist, Jan Baptista van Helmont, who first coined the word 'gas'. He was able to prepare carbon dioxide (then known as 'gas of the wood') from a wide range of ORGANIC MATERIALS (compounds of carbon), and from the action of an acid on seashells as well as from burning carbon-based materials.

Helmont was not able to collect and separate the gases he prepared because the apparatus for their preparation, and the techniques for collection, had not yet been developed. This was left to the Englishman, Stephen Hales. He separated the apparatus used to

GREAT EXPERIMENTAL SCIENTISTS
Robert Boyle

Robert Boyle (1627–1691) who, along with Lavoisier, is considered to be the father of chemistry was born at Lismore Castle, Munster, Ireland.

When his father died in 1644, Boyle returned to England and to a family estate in Dorset. In 1654 he went to Oxford, where he set up a small laboratory in his lodgings. In 1668, Boyle moved to London where he became a friend of Sir Isaac Newton and Samuel Pepys.

Boyle was a founder member of a group interested in widening knowledge. At first it was known as the Invisible College, but it later became the Royal Society, the world's first centre for scientific excellence.

Boyle is regarded as one of the foremost science experimenters. He also devised a definition of a chemical element, distinguished between mixtures and compounds and demonstrated that a compound may have very different properties to its components.

In 1660 (just 6 years before the Great Fire of London!) Boyle and his assistant, Robert Hooke, studied combustion and, using an air pump, effectively discovered that a substance (later found to be oxygen) was needed, and that this substance was not just in the air but could also be found in some solids, such as saltpetre (potassium nitrate). By 1680, he had discovered that, by coating coarse paper with phosphorus, a flame was produced when a sulphur-tipped splint was drawn through the folded paper. Boyle had invented the first match.

Boyle suggested the existence of simple atoms (which he called corpuscles) and that all phenomena could be explained in terms of the motion, shape, and position of these imperceptible particles.

Boyle also invented the term analysis and he introduced the plant extract, LITMUS, to test for acids and bases. He was one of the main scientists to transform chemistry from the mystic world of the ALCHEMIST into a science.

generate gases, for example, from the apparatus used to collect them. He developed the pneumatic trough, a simple, but specially designed piece of equipment and was then able to collect pure gases over water by downward displacement of air.

In 1766, Henry Cavendish was the first person to prepare hydrogen, and in 1774, Joseph Priestley, and Karl Scheele independently prepared and collected oxygen. Scheele went on to prepare other gases such as chlorine, while Priestley prepared ammonia, hydrogen chloride, the common oxides of nitrogen, and sulphur dioxide.

By this time it was clear that success in preparing more substances depended on accuracy and the use of pure reactants.

The 19th century saw the use of a new technique, involving the use of electricity. Sir Humphry Davy and Michael Faraday were the leaders in using the principles of electrolysis to separate COMPOUNDS and to prepare gases.

The majority of the substances investigated up to this time can be classed as INORGANIC SUBSTANCES. ORGANIC SUBSTANCES were the most recent to be investigated because of their complexity. It was only in the late 19th century that organic compounds were investigated.

GASES: Methods for preparing gases

Many chemical reactions yield gases as one of their products. COMBUSTION of a fuel, for example, generates a number of gases. This uncontrolled production of gases is, however, different from the preparation of a single, pure gas. To prepare a single gas you need to use pure reactants, in one specific reaction.

Methods for preparing gases

A gas may be prepared in three ways:
- by adding appropriate reactants to one another
- by heating a reactant
- by ELECTROLYSIS of an ELECTROLYTE

The reactants used will normally be chosen because they are appropriately cost effective and because they will generate the desired quantity of gas. Only commonly available reactants (reagents) are usually used in these demonstrations.

Choosing the apparatus

How the gas is to be prepared, how much gas is to be collected, and the nature of the gas produced, all influence the choice of apparatus used. For example, if a large amount of gas is to be prepared, say enough to fill a gas jar, then a much larger amount of reagent will be needed than that needed simply to test for the presence or nature of a gas. You will find examples of equipment suitable for the preparation of both small and large samples on these pages.

Preparing gases safely

Many of the gases commonly prepared in a laboratory are poisonous, even in low concentrations. It is therefore vital that gases are prepared and collected in a fume chamber and are never inhaled – not even as a way of identifying them. A separate volume in the ChemLab set explains how to identify gases safely.

Also, in addition to using a fume chamber, you also need to be able to control the rate of the reaction, so that the rate of gas production is matched by its safe collection. Remember that a gas can be compressed easily into a much smaller volume. If the design of the apparatus produces gas rapidly, the pressure that builds up in the system can be dangerous. Some gases are highly flammable and can explode if ignited.

The method used to control a reaction depends on the equipment being used. If two reactants react without the need for heat, then the reaction rate can be controlled by the rate at which one chemical is dropped on to another. If the reaction only works when heat is applied, then controlling the heat will control the reaction rate. Electrical heaters, known as 'heating mantles', can be used instead of Bunsen burners and thermostatically controlled, if close control of temperature is needed. Electrolytic reactions can be controlled easily by controlling the amount of current that is allowed to pass through the system.

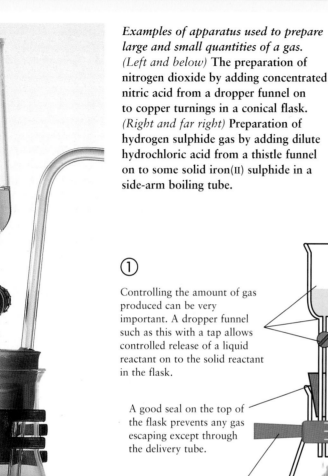

Examples of apparatus used to prepare large and small quantities of a gas. (Left and below) **The preparation of nitrogen dioxide by adding concentrated nitric acid from a dropper funnel on to copper turnings in a conical flask.** (Right and far right) **Preparation of hydrogen sulphide gas by adding dilute hydrochloric acid from a thistle funnel on to some solid iron(II) sulphide in a side-arm boiling tube.**

② The liquid reagent is poured in using a thistle funnel. As there is no tap, liquid must be added until it seals the end of the funnel stem (otherwise gas will escape up the funnel).

The boiling tube is clamped firmly.

The solid reactant is placed in a side-arm boiling tube.

Stem near base of tube so that it is quickly covered by liquid.

① Controlling the amount of gas produced can be very important. A dropper funnel such as this with a tap allows controlled release of a liquid reactant on to the solid reactant in the flask.

A good seal on the top of the flask prevents any gas escaping except through the delivery tube.

The apparatus should be held firmly in place with devices such as clamps secured to retort stands to prevent movement.

The gas being evolved passes along a delivery tube and may be collected, for example, in a gas jar.

In this case, a liquid reactant in the dropper funnel is being added to a solid reactant in a conical flask. However, liquids may be combined, a solid heated, or an electric current used to generate a gas.

Many reactions are EXOTHERMIC. Care should be taken to use heat-resistant supports for all apparatus.

The reaction vessel must be appropriate to the reactants used. A large vessel such as a conical flask with a side arm (known as a Büchner flask) is used where large quantities of gas are being produced, whereas a small vessel (such as a side-arm boiling tube) is best used for small quantities of reactants.

Choosing a suitable method

The most common way of producing a large amount of gas, such as that needed to fill a gas jar, is to use a dropper funnel and a conical or round-bottomed flask (①, page 9). If less gas is needed, then it is more economical to use a thistle funnel and a side-arm boiling tube (②, page 9).

Another common method of producing a gas is to decompose reactants in a boiling tube using heat (③). In a few cases, a gas can be prepared in a gas jar using a combustion spoon (④).

The apparatus required to generate a gas using electrolysis is more complicated and expensive than that used in any of the methods used above (⑤).

In all cases, gas can be transferred from the preparation apparatus either via a side arm, or by means of a delivery tube through a stopper.

Preparing a large, constant gas supply

Very large amounts of gas, or a constant flow of gas are best generated in a specialised apparatus known as Kipp's apparatus (⑥). This consists of three glass chambers placed to form a tower. The purpose of the apparatus is to allow a liquid reactant (usually an acid) from a reservoir in the upper container to run through the tube connecting it to the lowest container. The middle chamber contains the other reactant, which must be in the form of 'chips' or 'granules'.

The reaction is controlled by the tap in the middle chamber. When the tap is opened, the gas escapes and

③

(Above and right) **Preparation of gases using a heated, hard glass tube.** Some reactants can be made to decompose by heating. The boiling tube is held in a horizontal position for even heating. A delivery tube is taken through a stopper in the end of the tube.

④

(Right) **Preparation of gases using a combustion spoon.** Some gases can be prepared and collected in a gas jar. In this case, the solid is heated in the spoon and then introduced into a gas jar containing the gas it is to react with. Notice the special cover plate to prevent the gas escaping or air from entering.

liquid rises from the lower chamber and can react with the solid reactant, producing more gas. The gas builds up in the middle chamber, providing a reservoir of gas which can be accessed for experiments by opening the tap. If the tap is closed, the gas builds up, producing sufficient pressure to push the liquid reactant out of the middle container and back up into the reservoir. As the liquid is pushed away from the solid reactant, the reaction ceases and no more gas is produced. Thus, by opening and closing the tap, it is possible to produce and stop gas production at will (see also page 36).

⑤

Negative electrode (cathode)   Positive electrode (anode)

(Right) Preparation of gases using electrolysis. Many solutions conduct electricity (they are electrolytes) and by passing a direct electric current through them, ION migration occurs, with DECOMPOSITION to yield different products at each ELECTRODE. Electrolysis will produce small amounts of gases for laboratory use, but electrolysis is also used on an industrial scale if no other method of preparation is suitable.

Side-arm U-tube

Platinum electrodes do not CORRODE.

Bubbles of oxygen gas

A dilute solution of sulphuric acid is used.

Bubbles of hydrogen gas

(Below) Preparation of a gas using Kipp's apparatus.

⑥

This upper section (the reservoir) consists of a chamber containing a liquid reactant (usually acid) with a long tube projecting from its base.

Ground glass joint. This fits tightly into the lower part of the apparatus, while allowing the apparatus to be refilled with solid reactant when required.

The central section of the apparatus contains solid reactant in the form of granules. Notice that, with the tap turned off, the granules are not bathed in liquid reactant and so no reaction occurs.

The lowest chamber contains liquid reactant. The level of this reactant is controlled by the tap. Opening the tap allows gas to escape from the central chamber and this in turn allows the liquid reactant to rise and react with the granules, producing more gas. Closing the tap causes the gas pressure to build up, forcing the liquid back into the lowest chamber and stopping the reaction.

Methods for collecting gases

Gases are collected in four main ways:
• by downward displacement of air (for gases less dense – lighter – than air)
• by upward displacement of air (for gases denser – heavier – than air)
• over water (for insoluble gases)
• in a gas syringe (if the gas is to be measured)

A gas will fill up the space in any container, but in general, gases are collected in special glass cylinders called gas jars. Gas jars have a ground-glass lip; and when a thin disc of ground glass; a cover slip, is slid across the lip, it will produce a gas-tight fit. This allows the gas to be kept indefinitely.

Gases may also be collected in test tubes and boiling tubes. Neither of these types of containers has a ground glass lip and so gas can only be kept if the tubes are stoppered or if they are held vertically with the open end under water. Tubes are generally used when the gas is to be used immediately for some other purpose, such as for testing or reacting. The amount of gas that can be stored in tubes is small.

Collecting a gas by downward displacement of air

If the gas being generated is less dense than air (such as, for example, hydrogen), then it can be collected by downward displacement of air (①).

① *(Below)* **Hydrogen being collected by downward displacement of air.**

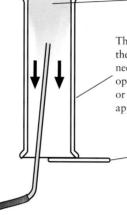

Delivery tube is positioned with the open end in the top of the collecting vessel.

The collecting vessel can differ in size depending on the volume of gas being produced or the amount that needs to be collected. It could be a gas jar (a thick-walled, open-ended jar especially made for containing gases) or for small quantities, some less specialised piece of apparatus, for example, a boiling tube may be appropriate.

A gas jar has a flat lip to allow the jar to be sealed using a glass cover slip. This is slid over the mouth once the required collection is complete. The cover slip and the jar lip each have ground glass surfaces to provide a leakproof fit.

(Below, left and right) **Illustration of downward displacement of a denser gas using nitrogen dioxide and air.**

During laboratory collections by downward displacement, it is air that is being displaced. The demonstration on this page has been done with a coloured gas, nitrogen dioxide, to illustrate what happens during this method of collection.

In this example, a gas jar was filled with brown nitrogen dioxide and then inverted. Oxygen was then generated and collected by downward displacement, displacing the nitrogen dioxide. In this sequence, the gas in the jar clearly gets a lighter colour as the nitrogen dioxide is displaced and then the remaining gas mixture is diluted.

This demonstration also shows some of the difficulties of simple displacement. Even if you follow all the rules, you don't tend to get a pure sample and there does tend to be some mixing. This is why collection over water is often preferred if the gas is not soluble in water and is not required to be dry.

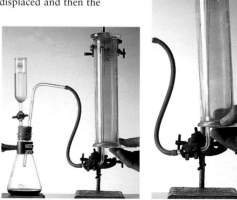

The delivery tube is taken to the top of an upturned gas jar or similar collecting system. This allows the gas to displace the air from the bottom.

Collecting a gas by upward displacement of air

If the gas being generated is more dense than air (carbon dioxide or chlorine, for example) then it can be collected by upward displacement of air (②). The gas is delivered to the bottom of a gas jar as shown in the diagram so that it displaces the air out of the top of the jar.

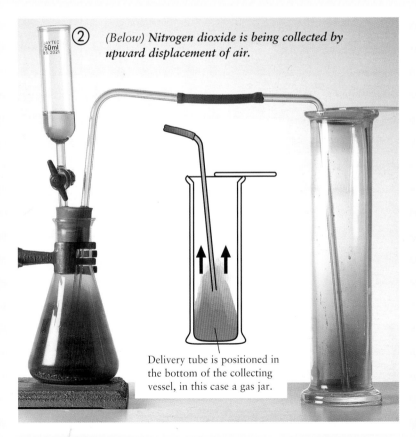

② *(Below) Nitrogen dioxide is being collected by upward displacement of air.*

Delivery tube is positioned in the bottom of the collecting vessel, in this case a gas jar.

(Right) A small quantity of gas can be collected in a boiling tube or test tube. Note the clamp used to hold the tube, rather than the hand. Many gases should not be allowed to come into contact with skin.

(Left) Sometimes the gas may need to be prepared but does not have to be collected. Here, the gas is being tested as it is being produced. When gas is allowed to escape from the system like this, however, it must always be done in the safety of a fume chamber.

In this case, the gas being tested was not harmful to the skin, and so a test strip of filter paper soaked in UNIVERSAL INDICATOR could be held in the fingers. However, when there is the slightest doubt about the nature of the gas, and especially if the gas is unknown, then protective gloves should always be worn.

③ *(Below) Collecting a gas over water.* The laboratory apparatus shown below is standard for collecting a large amount of a gas over water.

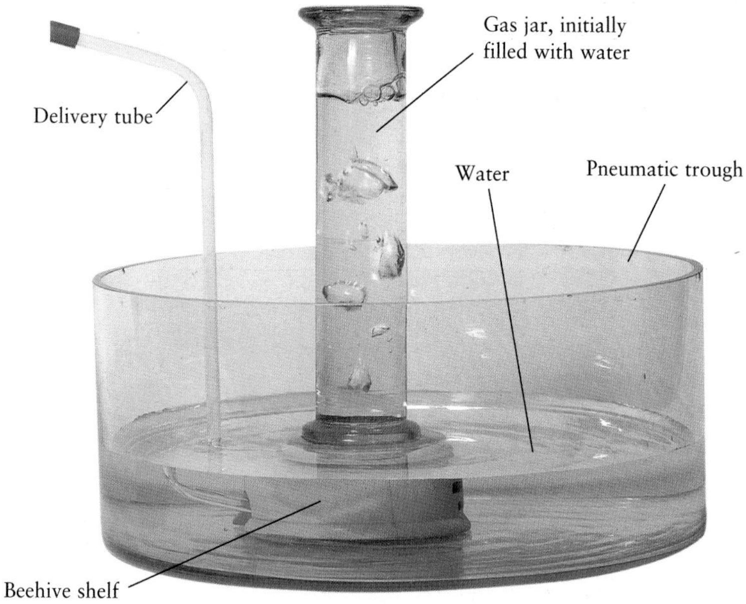

Delivery tube

Gas jar, initially filled with water

Water

Pneumatic trough

Beehive shelf

(Below, left and right) Small quantities of gas can be collected over water using a boiling tube or test tube filled with water and upturned in a small pneumatic trough or beaker.

The delivery tube is angled so that a boiling tube can be supported by the side of the trough. Alternatively, a tube can be held in a clamp.

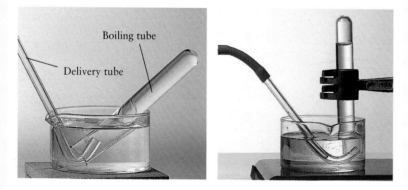

Boiling tube

Delivery tube

Collecting a gas over water

If the gas is insoluble or only slightly soluble, then it can be collected over water (③). The gas is delivered to the bottom of a gas jar or similar collecting container which has been filled with water and upturned in a PNEUMATIC TROUGH. As shown in the diagram, the upturned container may be placed over a BEEHIVE SHELF or simply placed over the end of the delivery tube. The less dense the gas, the greater the upward pressure that develops on the collecting flask. With gases considerably lighter than air, it may therefore be sensible to use heavier collecting containers, or to clamp the collecting vessel in place to prevent it capsizing.

Collecting a gas in a gas syringe

Small amounts of gas can also be collected in a GAS SYRINGE (④), a cylinder in which the piston is pushed out as the gas enters. This apparatus is usually used when the volume of gas produced is to be measured, but is also a convenient way of collecting a small sample.

④ *(Below)* Collection of a gas using a gas syringe.

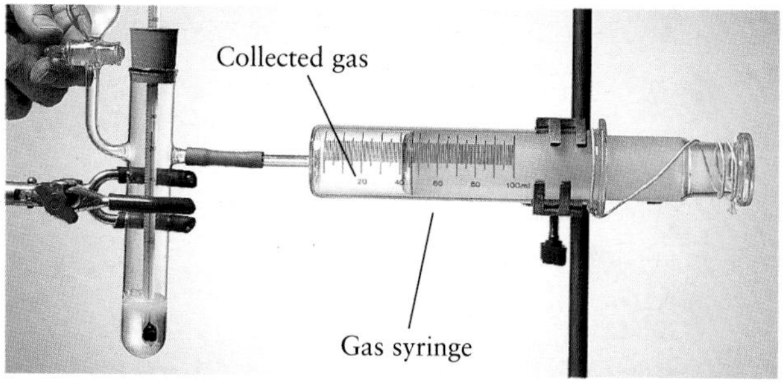

Collected gas

Gas syringe

Methods for drying gases

Some preparations produce the gas that is required, together with some water vapour, or one or more of the reagents is in aqueous solution. If dry gas is required, the water vapour must be removed from it

There are several methods for drying gases. They involve bubbling the gas through a liquid that will absorb water, for example, concentrated sulphuric acid or past a solid that absorbs water such as ANHYDROUS calcium chloride, anhydrous magnesium sulphate, copper sulphate or anhydrous cobalt chloride. Where a solid is used, it must be in granular, rather than in block or powder form. Granules have a larger surface area than a block of the same mass, while granules have larger spaces between them than powder, thus allowing a free flow of gas over the solid surface.

It is also important to remember that, once the drying agent has absorbed water, it must itself be dried again, for example, by heating a solid in an oven, before further use. Anhydrous copper sulphate and anhydrous cobalt chloride change colour as they take up moisture, making it easy to see whether or not the drying agent is still 'active'. Anhydrous cobalt chloride is often added to another drying agent (DESICCANT), silica gel, to show when it needs to be regenerated (wet cobalt chloride is pink).

(Below) A drying tower containing calcium oxide. This is an alternative apparatus to the U-tube, and calcium oxide is especially used to dry ammonia gas which reacts with some other common drying agents.

(Above) A guard tube allows gas to get in and out of a piece of equipment (and so prevent a build-up of pressure inside equipment) but doesn't allow moisture to get inside. A guard tube is often filled with the drying agent anhydrous calcium chloride.

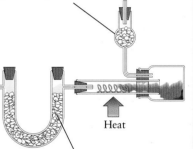

Heat

(Above) Drying agents are commonly placed in U-tubes. This U-tube is filled with drying agent of anhydrous calcium chloride.

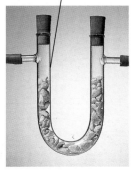

Inlet tube   Exit tube

(Left) A DRESCHEL BOTTLE containing sulphuric acid that is being used as a drying agent. The gas enters through the central tube inside the liquid and bubbles out before flowing through the exit tube.

Methods for separating gases

Molecules in a gas move faster than those in a liquid or solid. If two or more gases are placed in contact with each other, they mix. They are then often difficult to separate. There are few laboratory techniques available for the separation of gases. However, some gas mixtures may be separated if they have markedly different boiling points (①).

Sometimes it is possible to separate a gas by a chemical reaction, either by absorbing it in a SOLVENT or ADSORBING it on to a solid. Carbon dioxide, for example, is soluble in limewater (calcium hydroxide) and can be separated from air by bubbling the air through it (②). This is a convenient demonstration since what is formed is a PRECIPITATE that can easily be seen. Bromine can be separated from a mixture with oxygen using ACTIVATED CHARCOAL (③). The bromine is adsorbed on to the charcoal.

Another method which is commonly used in industry involves distillation of the liquid states of the gases, a process called fractional distillation. The separation of air into its principal components of oxygen, nitrogen and argon is a good example (④).

(Below) **In this demonstration, nitrogen dioxide is separated from a mixture with oxygen by cooling. The two gases are passed through a U-tube which has been placed in an ice bath. The nitrogen dioxide condenses out as a liquid. The U-tube has been taken out of the ice bath to show this. The oxygen, which does not liquefy until –169°C passes on out of the U-tube.**

①

② *(Above, left to right)* **In this demonstration, an air mixture is passed through limewater. Carbon dioxide is removed from the air as it reacts with the limewater solution to precipitate calcium carbonate, which makes the solution look milky.**

③ (*Below, from left to right*) **In this demonstration, pieces of activated charcoal have been dropped into a gas jar containing bromine and the cover slip replaced.**

The second picture shows that, within a minute, the colour of the gas is getting lighter as fewer free bromine molecules remain in the jar.

Finally, as shown in the third picture, after only a few minutes, the gas jar is colourless, because most of the bromine molecules are now adsorbed on to the surface of the activated charcoal with none remaining as free gas.

The air to be separated is pressurised and cooled to −190°C (just below the boiling point of each gas) in order to convert all the gases into their liquid states. The liquid is then passed through a fractionating column. Each of the gases that makes up the liquid air has a different boiling point. As the liquid air is warmed up, so each gas is released, in turn, into its VAPOUR or gaseous state and can be collected at different levels in a tower. Fractional distillation is further discussed on pages 56 and 57.

Because of the low temperatures involved, this method of separation is rarely used in the laboratory.

④

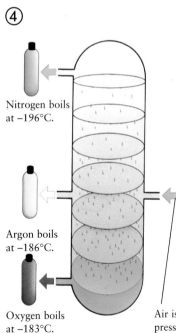

Nitrogen boils at −196°C.

Argon boils at −186°C.

Oxygen boils at −183°C.

(*Left*) **This diagram shows the industrial separation of air to obtain nitrogen, oxygen and argon.**

The liquid air is kept under a pressure of five atmospheres in the tower, at which pressure the boiling point of the nitrogen and oxygen are much higher, so it is easier to maintain them as liquids, than at normal atmospheric pressure which is around one atmosphere. The boiling points shown here are at normal atmospheric pressure.

Air is cooled to −190°C and pressurised to generate liquid air.

Preparation of hydrogen (H$_2$)

The standard procedure is to prepare hydrogen by reacting dilute acid with a reactive metal.

Demonstration: reaction of zinc with dilute hydrochloric acid

In this demonstration, dilute hydrochloric acid is dripped on to zinc. The reaction of zinc with acid is slow, but is greatly speeded up by the use of a CATALYST. The catalyst used here is copper, added in the form of copper(II) sulphate.

Pieces of zinc are placed in a conical flask. Notice that a considerable quantity of zinc has been used. The amount of zinc used is sufficient to produce several gas jars of hydrogen for subsequent experiments. The hydrochloric acid is poured into a dropper funnel which is fitted into the neck of the flask (①).

To provide the copper catalyst, a small amount of copper sulphate solution is added to the hydrochloric acid in the dropper funnel (②). It is the copper sulphate that contributes to the colour in the liquid in the dropper funnel.

When the dropper funnel tap is opened, the acid and copper catalyst flow on to the zinc. The reaction is vigorous, causing a fizzing as hydrogen is released (③). The rate of gas production is controlled by the amount of acid introduced.

Although hydrogen is less dense than air, it will mix with it and so the hydrogen should be collected over water (④). The hydrogen passes down a delivery tube and is collected in gas jars placed on a beehive shelf in a water bath. Once filled, a glass cover slip is slid over the open end of each gas jar while it is still down under the water, thus sealing the gas in the jar.

EQUATION 1: Preparation of hydrogen in the laboratory by the reaction of an acid and a metal

Hydrochloric acid + zinc ⇨ zinc chloride + hydrogen

$$2HCl(aq) + Zn(s) \Rightarrow ZnCl_2(aq) + H_2(g)$$

Catalyst, copper

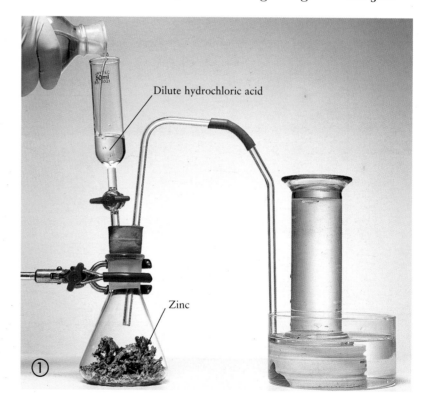

Dilute hydrochloric acid

Zinc

①

② Copper(II) sulphate is added.

Bubbles of hydrogen gas

④

③

Dilute hydrochloric acid and copper catalyst are released carefully from the dropper funnel and on to the zinc metal.

The hydrogen gas that is evolved is collected in a gas jar over water.

(Above) **Hydrogen gas burns with a colourless flame and at a high temperature, and tends to melt the glass around the end of the tube as it burns. The orange–red colour of the flame you see is due to the presence of sodium in the glass; the sodium colours the flame.**

The best test for hydrogen is to put the mouth of a hydrogen-filled gas jar to a flame. You get a high-pitched popping sound. Hydrogen will not relight a glowing splint.

PROPERTIES, USES AND INDUSTRIAL PRODUCTION OF HYDROGEN

Hydrogen gas is colourless, has no smell and is non-toxic. Hydrogen is highly flammable, burning with a colourless flame and explodes if allowed to mix with air and then be ignited.

Hydrogen has one-twelfth the density of air and will condense to its liquid state at −253°C. The resultant liquid is colourless and has one-tenth of the density of water. Hydrogen is not soluble in water at room temperature.

Hydrogen comprises about 99.88% of the Universe, but because it is so light it escaped from the Earth's atmosphere long ago and now makes up only 0.75% of our planet. On Earth, the vast majority of compounds formed with hydrogen are organic products derived from living organisms.

Hydrogen is produced industrially: (i) using the water gas method in which water is passed over white-hot coke (carbon), (ii) as 'synthesis gas' by steam re-forming natural gas, (iii) as a byproduct in oil refining and (iv) as a byproduct of the electrolysis of brine (a solution of sodium chloride) in Castner–Kellner, Down's or Diaphragm cells.

The hydrogen produced industrially is used mostly in the manufacture of ammonia-based fertilisers. However, large quantities of hydrogen are also used in the manufacture of hydrocarbons which, in turn, are used as key ingredients in many SYNTHETIC FIBRES.

Preparation of oxygen (O$_2$)

Oxygen is prepared by decomposing an oxygen-rich compound.

Demonstration 1: decomposing hydrogen peroxide

In this demonstration, black manganese dioxide powder is placed in the bottom of a conical flask. Manganese dioxide (MnO$_2$) is used as a catalyst and is essential for fast and steady release of oxygen. A dropper funnel is then attached to the flask. Hydrogen peroxide is poured into the dropper funnel (①). Using the tap on the dropper funnel, the hydrogen peroxide can then be dripped gradually on to the manganese dioxide powder. The hydrogen peroxide decomposes to liberate oxygen. The reaction is exothermic and the heat produced converts some of the water present to steam (②) and, because the reaction is rapid in the presence of the catalyst and at room temperature, no external heating of the reagents is required.

Pure oxygen is not easily collected by downward displacement of air as it is of a similar density to the mixture of gases that make up the air. If it not required to be dry, it can be collected over water using a gas jar, a beehive shelf and a pneumatic trough, as shown in this case. Oxygen is slightly soluble in water but not sufficiently so to prevent its collection over water.

EQUATION: Preparation of oxygen in the laboratory by decomposition of hydrogen peroxide

Hydrogen peroxide ⇨ *oxygen + water*

$$2H_2O_2(aq) \Rightarrow O_2(g) + 2H_2O(l)$$

Catalyst, MnO$_2$

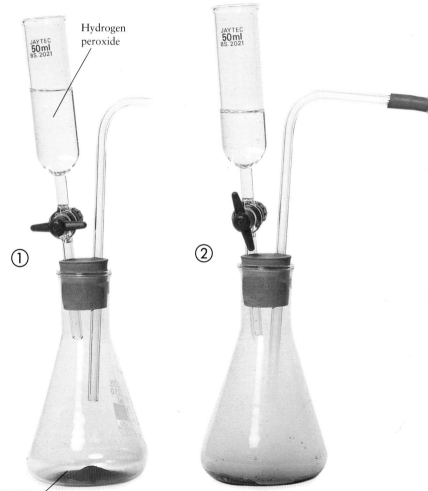

Hydrogen peroxide

① ②

Manganese dioxide powder

Demonstration 2: decomposition of potassium chlorate

Oxygen can also be prepared by the decomposition of oxygen-rich salts using heat (see equation below). In this demonstration, potassium chlorate ($KClO_3$), which is a white powder, is mixed with manganese dioxide, which is a black powder and acts as a catalyst.

The manganese dioxide lowers the temperature at which the potassium chlorate decomposes, reducing the chance of an explosive release of oxygen that can occur if the potassium chlorate is heated alone. The rekindling of a glowing splint (③ & ④) is, in part, a test that oxygen is being released. The only other common laboratory gas that will do this is nitrogen monoxide.

EQUATION: Preparation of oxygen in the laboratory by decomposition of potassium chlorate

Potassium chlorate ⇨ potassium chloride + oxygen

$2KClO_3(s) ⇨ 2KCl(s) + 3O_2(g)$

Catalyst, MnO_2

The splint is kept out of the potassium chlorate and manganese dioxide mixture.

Oxygen gas is collected.

PROPERTIES, USES AND INDUSTRIAL PRODUCTION OF OXYGEN

Oxygen gas is colourless and has no smell. Oxygen will support combustion and is one of the more reactive of the common elements.

Oxygen is slightly denser than air and will condense to its liquid state at −183°C. The resulting liquid is pale blue and a little denser than water. Oxygen is not very soluble in water at room temperature, but its limited solubility is vital to much aquatic life.

Oxygen makes up 21% of the volume of the atmosphere and is essential to living organisms, playing an important part in respiration and photosynthesis. Oxygen is required for the combustion of fuels such as methane, oil and coal.

Oxygen is produced industrially by the LIQUEFACTION and fractional distillation of air. Most oxygen produced industrially is used to refine iron to steel, in particular in the 'basic oxygen steelmaking process'. However, oxygen is also used in cutting and welding (e.g. in oxyacetylene torches), in the combustion of hydrogen and other fuels used to propel spacecraft, and in medicine to assist people having surgery and those with breathing difficulties.

Preparation of hydrogen (H₂) and oxygen (O₂)

Both hydrogen and oxygen can be prepared by electrolysis of appropriate electrolytes such as acidified water.

Demonstration: electrolysis of dilute sulphuric acid

Water that has been acidified will ionise, and such a solution will behave as an electrolyte. This means that water can be broken up or DISSOCIATED into its component elements by passing an electric current through it. An industrial version of this preparation method is used to produce very pure oxygen.

In this laboratory demonstration, a side-arm U-tube is fitted with two electrodes made of platinum. Each electrode passes through a stopper and is connected to a Direct Current (DC) power pack. The U-tube is filled with dilute sulphuric acid until the levels are a little way below the side

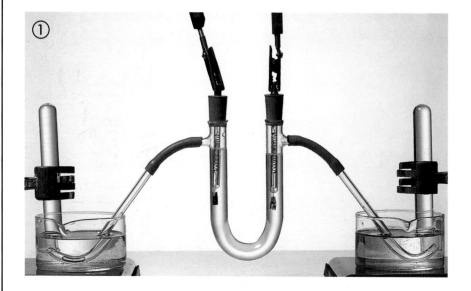

Negative electrode (cathode)

Positive electrode (anode)

②

Platinum electrodes do not corrode.

A dilute solution of sulphuric acid is used as the electrolyte.

Bubbles of hydrogen gas at the negative electrode

Bubbles of oxygen gas at the positive electrode

①

arms. Each side arm is connected to a delivery tube which, in turn, leads under an upturned boiling tube filled with water and supported in a pneumatic trough (①). The boiling tubes can be replaced by small gas jars if larger volumes of gases are required (see page 14).

As soon as the power supply is switched on, the ions in the solution are attracted to the electrodes. When the ions reach the electrodes, they either lose or take up electrons. Hydrogen ions, which are positively charged ions (CATIONS), migrate to the negative electrode, while the negative hydroxide ions (ANIONS) migrate to the positive electrode.

The exchange of electrons at the electrodes completes the electrical circuit and allows a current to flow. At the same time, the liberated oxygen atoms combine to form oxygen molecules (O_2 gas), and the liberated hydrogen atoms form hydrogen molecules (H_2 gas) (②). The gas generated can be seen as bubbles rising from the faces of the electrodes and being collected in the boiling tubes (③). In this demonstration, two volumes of hydrogen collect for every one volume of oxygen, thus confirming that the formula for water is H_2O (④).

OVERALL EQUATION: Preparation of hydrogen and oxygen in the laboratory by dissociation of water using electrolysis
Water ➪ hydrogen + oxygen
$2H_2O(l) ➪ 2H_2(g) + O_2(g)$
Electric current

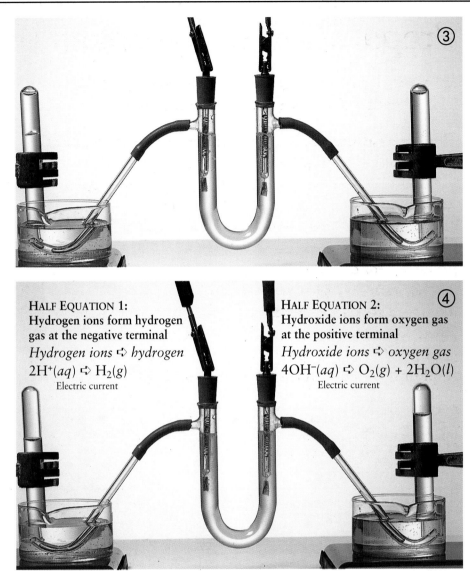

③

④

HALF EQUATION 1:
Hydrogen ions form hydrogen gas at the negative terminal
Hydrogen ions ➪ hydrogen
$2H^+(aq) ➪ H_2(g)$
Electric current

HALF EQUATION 2:
Hydroxide ions form oxygen gas at the positive terminal
Hydroxide ions ➪ oxygen gas
$4OH^-(aq) ➪ O_2(g) + 2H_2O(l)$
Electric current

NOTE: Pure water is a poor conductor of electricity as it consists only of water molecules (H_2O) with no impurities. However, the water we normally call pure water (meaning fit to drink) has many minerals dissolved in it, such as magnesium and calcium hydrogen carbonate. These minerals provide some ions to flow through the water and hence electrons move through the wires of the external circuit, causing an electric current. Acidified water does, however, produce a faster result.

Preparation of ammonia (NH₃)

Ammonia is prepared by heating a mixture of a BASE and a SALT.

Demonstration: reaction of ammonium sulphate and calcium hydroxide

Equal quantities of the salt and base are ground up and mixed using a pestle and mortar. The mixture is put into a long-necked, round-bottomed flask, and the neck clamped so that it points downwards (①).

EQUATION: Preparing ammonia in the laboratory
Ammonium sulphate + calcium hydroxide ⇨ ammonia + water + calcium sulphate
$(NH_4)_2SO_4(s) + Ca(OH)_2(s) \Rightarrow 2NH_3(g) + 2H_2O(l) + CaSO_4(s)$

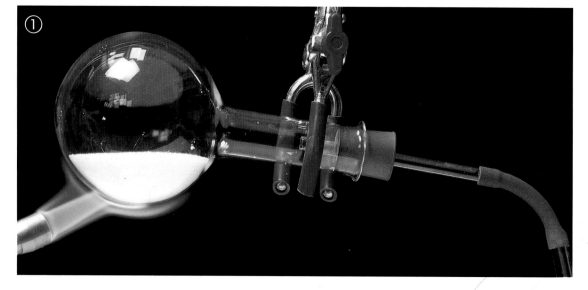
①

The mixture is heated. The heat energy causes a reaction and ammonia and water vapour are given off. If the ammonia is to be dissolved in water to make an ammonia solution, the delivery tube is connected to an upturned funnel so that the ammonia gas produced has a large surface area in which to dissolve into the water.

On the other hand, if the ammonia gas is to be used as dry gas for further demonstrations, the gas must be passed through a drying tower containing calcium oxide. The calcium oxide is another basic substance, so no reaction occurs with the ammonia. Note that many other drying agents, such as anhydrous calcium chloride or concentrated sulphuric acid, cannot be used as they form compounds with the ammonia.

The calcium oxide (quicklime) takes up the water from the ammonia (to make calcium hydroxide, slaked lime) and the dry ammonia gas is then collected by downward displacement of air because ammonia is less dense than air (see page 12). Due to its solubility, this gas cannot be collected over water.

Remarks

Ammonia is an extremely soluble alkaline gas that is often found in solution as a laboratory reagent called ammonia solution or ammonium hydroxide solution, as well as a household cleaning agent. One volume of water will dissolve four hundred times its own volume of ammonia. The density of the solution falls to 0.880 grams per millilitre as it becomes saturated and the solution is known as 880 ammonia. Ammonia gas is used in the fountain experiment to demonstrate the solubility of the gas, and can be used to detect the presence of hydrogen chloride gas, just as hydrogen chloride is used to detect the presence of ammonia. The reaction between these two gases produces a white smoke of ammonium chloride.

(Above) The presence of ammonia can be tested for by dipping a filter paper in hydrochloric acid and placing it just above the water. As ammonia is released from the water, so the reaction of the ammonia and the escaping hydrogen chloride gas produces a characteristic white smoke.

PROPERTIES, USES AND INDUSTRIAL PRODUCTION OF AMMONIA

Ammonia is colourless and has a pungent smell and is choking when inhaled but is not poisonous. Ammonium carbonate crystals release ammonia and are used as 'smelling salts'. Ammonia is not flammable in air but will combine with oxygen.

Ammonia is much less dense than air and will condense to its liquid state at –33°C; the resultant liquid is colourless and slightly less dense than water. Ammonia is extremely soluble in water giving an alkaline solution. Ammonia is the only common 'alkaline' gas.

A solution of ammonia in water is sold commercially as 'household ammonia' and is used for cleaning and as a disinfectant. The main use of ammonia, however, is in the production of nitric acid and in the preparation of artificial nitrogen-containing fertilisers.

The industrial method of making ammonia is called the Haber–Bosch process after its inventors. In the process (*see diagram below*), nitrogen and hydrogen gases are reacted at temperatures up to 600°C and high pressures (up to 600 atmospheres). The reaction works best if this is done in the presence of iron, which acts as a catalyst in the reaction and so remains unchanged.

In the main chamber, nitrogen and hydrogen are passed over finely divided iron, which acts as a catalyst. The tower is designed to provide a very large surface area on which the gases can react in the presence of the catalyst. In this chamber, much of the hydrogen and nitrogen is converted to ammonia.

Hydrogen

Nitrogen

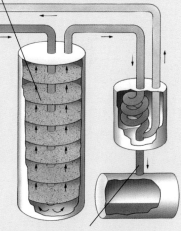

The mixture of gases is put under great pressure and heated to a higher temperature.

EQUATION: Production of ammonia by the Haber–Bosch process

Hydrogen + nitrogen ⇨ ammonia

$$3H_2(g) + N_2(g) \rightleftharpoons 2NH_3(g)$$
Pressure and heat

The gases are cooled, and ammonia is liquefied and drawn off from the base of the cooling chamber. The unreacted gases are recycled back to the catalytic chamber.

Preparation of nitrogen dioxide (NO$_2$)

The most convenient method of producing nitrogen dioxide gas is to react nitric acid with a suitable metal. Nitric acid is used because it is also a strong oxidising agent.

Nitrogen dioxide can also be prepared by decomposing a nitrogen-rich compound. It is helpful to use a compound of a less reactive metal, because its compounds will not be very stable and they will decompose relatively easily.

Demonstration 1: reaction of nitric acid and copper

Nitrogen dioxide can be generated in large quantities suitable for filling a gas jar, or in small quantities in a boiling tube. To produce a large quantity of the gas, a conical flask and a dropper funnel are used. The demonstration shows the use of copper, in the form of copper turnings (① & ②). The benefit of using turnings, or shavings of copper is that they present a large surface area and allow the reaction to proceed more quickly than if a solid piece of copper is used.

As the nitric acid is added from the dropper funnel, the reaction takes place without the need for external heating or a catalyst and brown nitrogen

① Copper turnings

② Concentrated nitric acid

③

EQUATION: Preparation of nitrogen dioxide
Copper + nitric acid ⇨ copper nitrate + water + nitrogen dioxide
$Cu(s) + 4HNO_3(conc) ⇨ Cu(NO_3)_2(aq) + 2H_2O(l) + 2NO_2(g)$

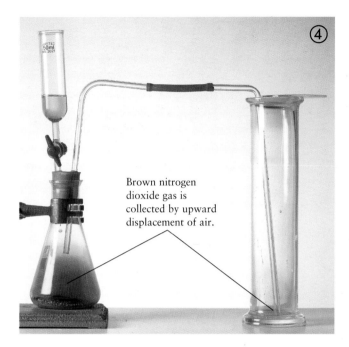

④

Brown nitrogen dioxide gas is collected by upward displacement of air.

dioxide gas is generated (③). In this demonstration the delivery tube is taken through the stopper in the flask, but a side-arm flask could be used equally well.

Nitrogen dioxide is heavier than air and so can be collected by upward displacement (see page 13). It is important that the delivery tube is long enough to reach to the bottom of the gas jar (④). This produces the most efficient displacement of air.

The gas is a deep brown colour and so it can be readily observed in the gas jar. When the gas jar is coloured uniformly, the delivery tube is lifted out and a glass cover slip is slipped over the gas jar to prevent air mixing with the nitrogen dioxide (⑤).

Remarks

Nitrogen dioxide dissolves in water to form a solution of nitric acid which is colourless if dilute. Because of its solubility, nitrogen dioxide cannot be collected over water.

⑤

PROPERTIES AND ENVIRONMENTAL IMPACT OF NITROGEN DIOXIDE

Nitrogen dioxide is a brown, pungent smelling and very poisonous gas. Nitrogen dioxide is reactive. It normally occurs along with N_2O_4 (see page 29).

Nitrogen dioxide is over one and a half times denser than air and will condense to its liquid state at –10°C. Nitrogen dioxide is soluble in water at room temperature and forms a solution of nitric acid and nitrogen monoxide.

Nitrogen dioxide and the other oxides of nitrogen (collectively known as NO_x, pronounced 'nox' gases) including dinitrogen oxide (nitrous oxide) and nitrogen monoxide (nitric oxide) are produced in car engines and are some of the most important primary pollutants of the atmosphere contributing to acid rain and smog. In photochemical smog, nitrogen dioxide causes irritation to the lungs, assists in the formation of (nitrate) particles that reduce visibility and aids the generation of ozone which in turn is harmful.

(Below) The nitrogen dioxide gas is acidic and so will turn filter paper soaked in Universal Indicator bright red. However, unlike the similarly brown gas bromine, nitrogen dioxide will only slowly bleach the paper.

Demonstration 2: decomposition of lead nitrate

The apparatus consists of a boiling tube in which the gases will be generated. This is connected through a delivery tube to a side-arm U-tube, where the nitrogen dioxide will be liquefied and collected. The apparatus may be completed by a boiling tube filled with water (⑥) and inverted in a small pneumatic trough, where the oxygen is collected over water if it is required.

Lead nitrate, which is a white powder, is placed in the boiling tube and heated. The powder melts to form lead oxide (⑦). The bubbles are oxygen and various oxides of nitrogen but the brown fumes that colour the liquid are nitrogen dioxide. As the lead nitrate decomposes, considerable amounts of energy are involved, which can be heard as cracking noises as the crystals of lead nitrate break up, a process called decrepitation.

The gases released enter the U-tube, which is kept in an ice bath so that the nitrogen dioxide will condense into a liquid (⑧). The oxygen, which does not liquefy until −169°C, will pass on to be collected (if required) in the final boiling tube. Warming the contents of the U-tube releases the nitrogen dioxide gas.

Remarks

This apparatus has been selected to illustrate that many variations in design are possible. In this case, advantage has been taken of the fact that nitrogen dioxide boils at about 18°C and so will liquefy if cooled in an ice bath. The apparatus used here allows the

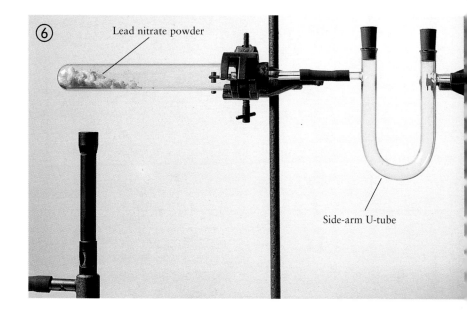

nitrogen dioxide to be collected as a liquid that can easily be converted to a gas (⑨). The pneumatic trough can be omitted from the set-up and the nitrogen dioxide can be collected by upward displacement of air as in the previous demonstration, although it will be mixed with oxygen.

EQUATION: Preparation of nitrogen dioxide by the decomposition of lead nitrate
Lead nitrate ➪ lead oxide + nitrogen dioxide + oxygen
$2Pb(NO_3)_2(s) ➪ 2PbO(s) + 4NO_2(g) + O_2(g)$

⑦

(Above) Due to its molecular structure, nitrogen dioxide normally occurs with a proportion of what is called its dimer, dinitrogen tetroxide (N_2O_4). Nitrogen dioxide is a brown gas and when cooled becomes dinitrogen tetroxide which forms a yellow liquid. However, the liquid that has been taken out of the ice bath is green. This is thought to be caused by a blue impurity N_2O_3 formed from NO_2 and NO (also produced in the decomposition).

The condensed liquid can be poured into a flask. When immersed in hot water, brown nitrogen dioxide fumes are given off.

Preparation of nitrogen monoxide (NO)

Nitrogen monoxide, also called nitric oxide, is a colourless gas that is virtually insoluble in water. The gas can be prepared by reacting dilute nitric acid with a metal.

Demonstration: reaction of nitric acid and copper

In this demonstration, a small amount of nitrogen monoxide is prepared in a side-arm boiling tube with a thistle funnel. Dilute nitric acid is poured through the thistle funnel on to copper turnings (①).

No external source of heating is required. The acid and the copper react releasing a colourless gas whilst the solution of copper nitrate turns a blue–green. The gas can be collected over water from a delivery tube fitted to the side arm (see page 13).

EQUATION: Preparation of nitrogen monoxide

Dilute nitric acid + copper ⇨ copper nitrate + nitrogen monoxide + water

$8HNO_3(aq) + 3Cu(s) ⇨ 3Cu(NO_3)_2(aq) + 2NO(g) + 4H_2O(aq)$

PROPERTIES, USES AND INDUSTRIAL PRODUCTION OF NITROGEN MONOXIDE

Nitrogen monoxide is a colourless gas. Nitrogen monoxide will not support combustion and is rapidly oxidised by the oxygen in air to form brown fumes of nitrogen dioxide (see page 26).

Nitrogen monoxide is only very slightly denser than air, virtually insoluble in water at room temperature and is neutral.

Nitrogen monoxide is produced naturally during lightning flashes in the atmosphere. It is also an important pollutant as it is one of the oxides of nitrogen (NO_x gases) produced by combustion engines. It is readily oxidised to nitrogen dioxide which contributes to photochemical smog. It therefore contributes to acid rain and, like chlorofluorocarbons, contributes to the destruction of the ozone layer.

Nitrogen monoxide is produced industrially during the manufacture of nitric acid in the Oswald process. However, this gas may also be produced industrially using the same method as that used in the laboratory of adding dilute nitric acid to copper.

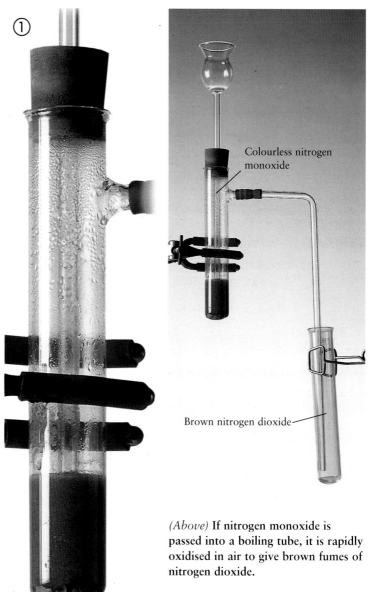

① Colourless nitrogen monoxide

Brown nitrogen dioxide

(Above) If nitrogen monoxide is passed into a boiling tube, it is rapidly oxidised in air to give brown fumes of nitrogen dioxide.

Preparation of hydrogen sulphide (H₂S)

Hydrogen sulphide can be prepared by reacting an acid with a metal sulphide.

Hydrogen sulphide is soluble in water but, because it is denser than air, it can be collected in a gas jar by upward displacement of air.

Demonstration: reaction of hydrochloric acid and iron(II) sulphide

Hydrogen sulphide is a poisonous gas and so should be prepared in a fume chamber even when required only in small quantities. To prepare a small quantity, a side-arm boiling tube and a thistle funnel are used.

Some iron(II) sulphide solid is first put into the boiling tube, then the stopper and thistle funnel are fitted. Dilute hydrochloric acid is then poured slowly through the thistle funnel (①). No external source of heating is required. As the acid and the iron sulphide react, so a vigorous bubbling occurs and a yellow solution of iron(II) chloride forms (②). The gas is collected by fitting a delivery tube to the side arm (see page 14).

EQUATION: Preparation of hydrogen sulphide
Dilute hydrochloric acid + iron(II) sulphide ⇨ iron(III) chloride + hydrogen sulphide
$2HCl(aq) + FeS(s) \Rightarrow FeCl_2(aq) + H_2S(g)$

① ②

PROPERTIES, USES AND INDUSTRIAL PRODUCTION OF HYDROGEN SULPHIDE

Hydrogen sulphide is a colourless gas which even at very low concentrations has an irritating and pungent smell of rotten eggs. It is also extremely poisonous, causing paralysis of the nervous system. Hydrogen sulphide will burn with a blue flame. A mixture of hydrogen sulphide and air is dangerous because it can be explosive.

Hydrogen sulphide is slightly denser than air and will condense to its liquid state at −60°C. Hydrogen sulphide is soluble in water at room temperature.

Due to its reactivity, hydrogen sulphide is not common in the atmosphere but is a product of organic decay and is generated in hot springs giving them their characteristic smell. Hydrogen sulphide can also be found in petroleum and most of the industrial needs for the gas are met by collecting it as a byproduct of petroleum refining. Most of the hydrogen sulphide that is produced industrially is converted to oxides of sulphur and used to manufacture sulphuric acid.

Hydrogen sulphide is a very strong reducing agent and, when reacted with other compounds, forms sulphides that are characteristically black in colour. There are exceptions such as cadmium sulphide, which is orange.

(Right) When hydrogen sulphide gas is bubbled into lead acetate, the solution is immediately converted to lead sulphide and a black precipitate forms. This test confirms the presence of hydrogen sulphide.

Preparation of hydrogen chloride gas (HCl)

There are two common ways of preparing the gas: by reacting the gases hydrogen and chlorine, and by reacting a metal chloride and concentrated sulphuric acid.

Demonstration 1: burning hydrogen in chlorine

Chlorine gas is produced by the method shown on page 34. Hydrogen is produced by the method shown on page 18. The hydrogen gas is ignited at a jet and introduced into a gas jar containing chlorine gas (①). The hydrogen burns with a white flame.

The hydrogen and chlorine react to produce hydrogen chloride gas, which then attracts water and forms a white mist of extremely corrosive hydrochloric acid droplets.

Demonstration 2: reacting concentrated sulphuric acid and a sodium chloride

The apparatus in this demonstration is used to produce a small amount of hydrogen chloride gas. A metal chloride, in this case sodium chloride (the main component of common salt) is placed in the bottom of a side-arm boiling tube. Concentrated sulphuric acid is added slowly through a thistle funnel (②). The sulphuric acid displaces the hydrogen chloride as a gas (③). The reaction produces considerable effervescence and does not need external heating.

Remarks

Hydrogen chloride is a corrosive gas that fumes strongly in moist air. It is extremely soluble in water. Hydrogen chloride gas is colourless. The white fumes seen in these pictures are produced as the gas comes into contact with moist air and forms small droplets of hydrochloric acid.

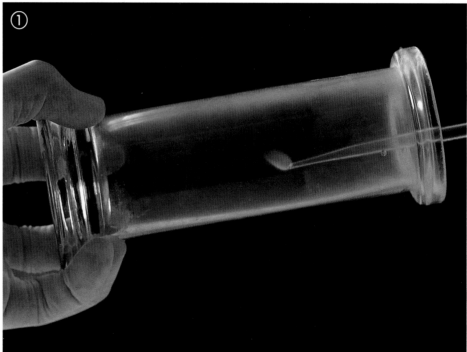

EQUATION: Preparation of hydrogen chloride gas by burning hydrogen in chlorine
Hydrogen + chlorine ⇨ hydrogen chloride gas
$H_2(g) + Cl_2(g) \Rightarrow 2HCl(g)$

EQUATION: Preparation of hydrogen chloride gas by reacting concentrated sulphuric acid with sodium chloride
Sulphuric acid + sodium chloride ⇨ sodium hydrogen sulphate + hydrogen chloride gas
$H_2SO_4(conc) + NaCl(s) ⇨ NaHSO_4(s) + HCl(g)$

Concentrated
sulphuric acid

②

③

Sodium chloride powder

(Right and far right)
If hydrogen chloride gas is bubbled through silver nitrate and dilute nitric acid solution, a precipitate of white silver chloride is produced (which is insoluble in water). This is one of the tests used to identify that the gas produced is hydrogen chloride.

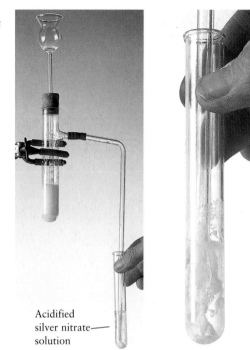

Acidified
silver nitrate
solution

PROPERTIES, USES AND INDUSTRIAL PRODUCTION OF HYDROGEN CHLORIDE

Hydrogen chloride gas is colourless and pungent smelling. However, if any of the gas is inhaled, it produces immediate, severe irritation of the nose and throat because it dissolves in the mucous membranes and immediately turns into hydrochloric acid.

Hydrogen chloride is a little denser than air and will condense to its liquid state at −85°C. The resultant liquid is a pale yellow colour and twice as dense as water. Hydrogen chloride is very soluble in water at room temperature and yields an acidic solution of hydrochloric acid.

Hydrogen chloride is rare in nature, occurring around the vents of active volcanoes.

However, hydrogen chloride is produced in large quantities industrially by burning hydrogen in chlorine using charcoal as a catalyst. The hydrogen chloride produced can be used either as a gas or in an aqueous state (dissolved in water) as hydrochloric acid. It has many uses, including the manufacture of plastics, extracting metals from their ores and for cleaning steel. Hydrochloric acid is also a common laboratory reagent. The concentrated acid contains 38% hydrogen chloride.

Preparation of chlorine (Cl$_2$)

Chlorine may be prepared from hydrochloric acid, either by reacting it with an oxidising agent or a bleach.

Demonstration 1: preparation by oxidising concentrated hydrochloric acid using potassium permanganate

The apparatus consists of a dropper funnel and a conical flask. Purple crystals of potassium permanganate are placed in the flask and the stopper is fitted tightly. Concentrated hydrochloric acid is dripped on to the crystals.

A green-coloured gas immediately begins to fill the flask and then flows out into the gas jar (①). At first the colour in the gas jar is pale yellow–green, but as more gas flows in it begins to deepen. When the jar is full of green gas, the colour ceases to deepen, the delivery tube is taken out, and the gas jar sealed with a glass cover slip.

①

Concentrated hydrochloric acid

Potassium permanganate

Yellow–green chlorine gas

EQUATION: Preparation of chlorine by oxidation of hydrochloric acid using potassium permanganate

Concentrated hydrochloric acid + potassium permanganate ⇨ chlorine + water + manganese(II) chloride + potassium chloride

$16HCl(conc) + 2KMnO_4(s) \Rightarrow 5Cl_2(g) + 8H_2O(l) + 2MnCl_2(aq) + 2KCl(aq)$

Demonstration 2: reacting dilute hydrochloric acid with bleach

Chlorine can also be prepared by reacting dilute hydrochloric acid and sodium chlorate (bleach) solution. In this demonstration, a thistle funnel is used together with a side-arm boiling tube (②). The sodium chlorate solution is poured into the boiling tube and the stopper, together with the thistle funnel, are pushed firmly into the top of the tube. The hydrochloric acid is then poured slowly into the thistle funnel.

The gas in the boiling tube will be slightly green, a much weaker colour than when the method using potassium permanganate is used. This is because fewer gas molecules are held in a boiling tube than in a conical flask, and so the 'greenness' of the gas is less striking.

If the chlorine is to be collected, a delivery tube can be connected to the side arm. If the gas is simply to be used for testing (as is shown in the picture on the right), then the delivery tube is not needed.

Remarks

Because chlorine is poisonous, the gas must always be prepared in a fume chamber.

Chlorine is a green gas that is denser than air and very soluble in water. It is therefore usually collected by upward displacement of air.

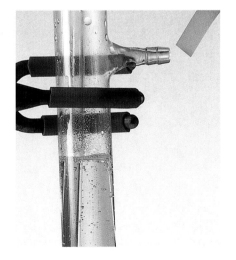

Chlorine is a distinctive greenish-yellow colour. It is a powerful oxidising agent which can be tested as it turns colourless potassium iodide solution on filter paper brown and will also turn damp green pH paper red before rapidly bleaching the paper *(right)*.

PROPERTIES, USES AND INDUSTRIAL PRODUCTION OF CHLORINE

Chlorine gas is greenish-yellow, has a pungent smell, irritates the membranes of the nose at very low concentrations and at only slightly higher concentrations, it causes difficulty in breathing. A flame will continue to burn in chlorine.

Chlorine has almost two and a half times the density of air and will condense to its liquid state at $-34°C$, the resultant liquid is greenish-yellow and denser than water. Chlorine is slightly soluble in water at room temperature forming hydrochloric (HCl) and hypochlorous ($HOCl$) acids.

Chlorine gas is highly reactive, forming compounds and so is never found naturally in its elemental state. It can be found as sodium chloride in sea water and in rocks.

Chlorine is one of the ten most important industrial chemicals and is produced by the electrolysis of brine (a solution of sodium chloride) or molten sodium chloride using Castner-Kellner, Down's or Diaphragm electrolytic cells.

The chlorine produced is used mostly as a water disinfectant and in the manufacture of explosives, bleaches, solvents and organic chemicals, in general, but, plastics (such as polyvinyl chloride or PVC), in particular.

EQUATION: Preparation of chlorine using dilute hydrochloric acid and a bleach
Dilute hydrochloric acid + sodium chlorate(I) ⇨ chlorine + sodium chloride + water
$2HCl(aq) + NaOCl(aq) \Rightarrow Cl_2(g) + 2NaCl(aq) + H_2O(l)$

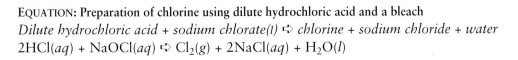

Preparation of carbon dioxide (CO_2)

Carbon dioxide gas can be produced by reacting an acid with a carbonate. Here, the opportunity is taken to demonstrate contrasting methods for producing a constant stream of gas, or for producing small quantities.

Demonstration 1: reaction of hydrochloric acid with calcium carbonate in Kipp's apparatus

Marble chips are placed in the middle chamber of Kipp's apparatus (see also page 11) (① & ②). The upper reservoir is fitted and the dilute hydrochloric acid added. The tap is then opened to allow the air in the middle chamber to escape (③). At the same time,

acid flows from the reservoir, fills the lowest chamber and then flows up the narrow gap separating the lowest from the middle chamber. Here, the acid can react with the marble chips (④, page 38). As the acid level rises in the middle container, the marble chips and acid react, causing rapid effervescence.

The reaction produces carbon dioxide gas, calcium chloride and water. The gas builds up in the middle chamber, providing a reservoir of carbon

PROPERTIES, USES AND INDUSTRIAL PRODUCTION OF CARBON DIOXIDE

Carbon dioxide is a colourless gas with no smell. Carbon dioxide is not particularly reactive and does not burn or support combustion.

Carbon dioxide is denser than air and will condense directly to its solid state (dry ice) at −79°C. Carbon dioxide is slightly soluble in water at room temperature, forming a weak acid, carbonic acid (H_2CO_3).

Carbon dioxide makes up about 0.03% air in the Earth's atmosphere, and is used naturally by plants in photosynthesis. It is also formed by the action of an acid on a carbonate, for example, natural rainwater on limestone.

There are many sources of industrial carbon dioxide, such as the production

of quicklime from limestone and in the production of coke. The combustion of carbon and most compounds containing carbon in the presence of a plentiful supply of oxygen will produce carbon dioxide.

Most industrially produced carbon dioxide is used for freezing in the form of dry ice which SUBLIMES at −78°C. Carbon dioxide is also dissolved in certain drinks under pressure to make them carbonated (fizzy). The gas adds to the sharp flavour of the drink, and when the bottle top is removed, the reduction in pressure allows much of the carbon dioxide to come out of solution and give the fizz. When sugars ferment, carbon dioxide is given off and alcohol is produced.

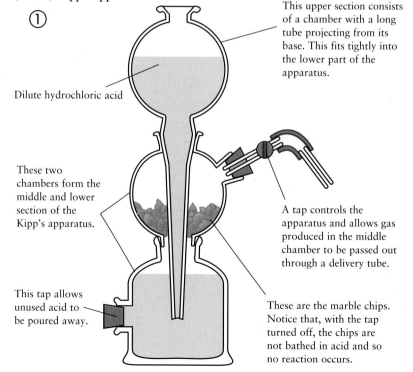

(Below) Kipp's apparatus

①

This upper section consists of a chamber with a long tube projecting from its base. This fits tightly into the lower part of the apparatus.

Dilute hydrochloric acid

These two chambers form the middle and lower section of the Kipp's apparatus.

This tap allows unused acid to be poured away.

A tap controls the apparatus and allows gas produced in the middle chamber to be passed out through a delivery tube.

These are the marble chips. Notice that, with the tap turned off, the chips are not bathed in acid and so no reaction occurs.

dioxide gas. When the tap is closed, the gas builds up, producing sufficient pressure to push the acid out of the middle chamber (⑤, page 38), away from the marble chips and back up into the reservoir. As the acid is pushed away from the chips, the reaction ceases and no more gas is produced. Thus, by opening and closing the tap, it is possible to produce and stop the production of carbon dioxide at will.

The carbon dioxide gas, which is more dense than air, can then be collected either by upward displacement of air or over water (see pages 13 and 14).

EQUATION: Preparation of carbon dioxide gas
Dilute hydrochloric acid + calcium carbonate ⇨ calcium chloride + carbon dioxide + water
$2HCl(aq) + CaCO_3(s) \Rightarrow CaCl_2(aq) + CO_2(g) + H_2O(l)$

③

②

This tap is tightly wired on to the chamber to prevent the gas pressure inside the chamber from pushing it out of the chamber.

Delivery tube

Marble chips

(*Above*) This picture shows the Kipp's apparatus when the tap has been turned on. The bottom chamber is now completely full of acid, and acid has risen inside the middle chamber and is reacting with the marble. Considerable fizzing can be seen, the gas produced being carbon dioxide.

(*Above*) The tap is turned off, causing the gas pressure to increase and the acid to be forced back down into the bottom chamber. The middle chamber now contains carbon dioxide gas (compare to the starting state when it contained air). The gas can be used at any time.

Demonstration 2: reaction of hydrochloric acid with sodium carbonate in a boiling tube

Sodium carbonate (a white powder) is placed in the boiling tube and dilute hydrochloric acid added via the thistle funnel (⑥).

An external source of heat is not required, and as soon as the acid and carbonate react, rapid effervescence of carbon dioxide occurs. This is taken for use via a delivery tube attached to the side arm.

Remarks

Although in principle any acid reacts with any carbonate to release carbon dioxide, a combination of dilute hydrochloric acid and marble chips is preferred in Kipp's apparatus. If sulphuric acid were used, then the reaction would produce calcium sulphate as one of the products. Calcium sulphate is not very soluble and as it precipitated on the marble chips, the coating of calcium sulphate would stop the sulphuric acid reacting further with the calcium carbonate of the chips and gas production would stop. Calcium chloride, on the other hand, is very soluble.

For a faster reaction, sodium carbonate is used in the boiling tube demonstration. The amount of gas produced from the reactants in a boiling tube is really only suited to testing purposes. Enough carbon dioxide to fill a gas jar could best be obtained by using a conical flask and a dropper funnel.

Carbon dioxide gas is not poisonous and it does not need to be prepared in a fume chamber.

EQUATION 2: Preparation of carbon dioxide
Sodium carbonate + hydrochloric acid ⇨ sodium chloride + water
$$Na_2CO_3(s) + 2HCl(aq) \rightarrow 2NaCl(aq) + H_2O(l) + CO_2(g)$$

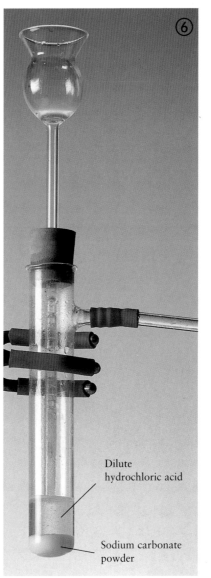

Dilute hydrochloric acid

Sodium carbonate powder

(Below) **If carbon dioxide is bubbled through a boiling tube of calcium hydroxide solution (limewater), the carbon dioxide causes the colourless limewater *(left)* to turn cloudy with particles of the precipitated calcium carbonate *(right)*. This is regarded as a laboratory test for carbon dioxide.**

However, if an excess is added, then the suspension goes clear and colourless again as the calcium carbonate is converted into soluble calcium hydrogen carbonate ($Ca(HCO_3)_2$ - calcium bicarbonate).

Boiling this solution will turn the solution cloudy again as the calcium hydrogen carbonate is converted back into calcium carbonate.

Limewater

Preparation of carbon monoxide (CO)

Carbon monoxide can readily be prepared by dehydrating methanoic acid, by oxidising carbon, or by reducing carbon dioxide. The gas is not soluble and can be collected over water.

Demonstration 1: dehydration of methanoic acid using concentrated sulphuric acid

Carbon monoxide may be prepared by reacting sulphuric acid and sodium methanoate (sodium formate, HCOONa). The apparatus used here is a dropper funnel and a conical flask. The delivery tube leads out of the flask and into a pneumatic trough so that the gas can be collected in a gas jar over water.

Sodium methanoate powder is placed in the conical flask (①) and concentrated sulphuric acid dripped on to it from the dropper funnel (②). No external heat source is required for this reaction.

The reaction produces methanoic (formic) acid. The presence of excess concentrated sulphuric acid then acts as a dehydrating agent. The formula for methanoic acid is HCOOH. The dehydrating process removes water (H_2O) leaving carbon monoxide (CO) as the other product. The carbon monoxide can then be collected.

EQUATIONS: Preparation of carbon monoxide using sulphuric acid and sodium methanoate

Sodium methanoate + sulphuric acid ⇨ formic acid + sodium sulphate
$$2HCOONa(aq) + H_2SO_4(conc) ⇨ 2HCOOH(l) + Na_2SO_4(aq)$$

Formic acid ⇨ carbon monoxide + water
$$HCOOH(l) ⇨ CO(g) + H_2O(l)$$
Sulphuric acid ($H_2SO_4(conc)$) as dehydrating agent

(Left) **Carbon monoxide burns with a characteristic blue flame.**

①

PROPERTIES, USES AND INDUSTRIAL PRODUCTION OF CARBON MONOXIDE

Carbon monoxide is a colourless gas with no smell.

Carbon monoxide is extremely toxic, competing with oxygen to be carried by haemoglobin in the blood and forming compounds that block further oxygen uptake. Thus, when people breathe in carbon monoxide, they are deprived of the oxygen they need. It may affect alertness and at concentrations of 10% of the air by volume it is fatal within a few minutes.

Carbon monoxide will burn with a blue flame.

Carbon monoxide is about the same density as air and is almost insoluble in water at room temperature. It is readily oxidised.

Carbon monoxide is produced by the combustion of carbon or carbon compounds in a restricted oxygen (air) supply. (Complete combustion would oxidise the carbon or carbon compounds to carbon dioxide.) A typical combustion engine can produce about a tenth of its exhaust gases as carbon monoxide.

Carbon monoxide is produced industrially by passing steam over white-hot coke. This produces a mixture of hydrogen and carbon monoxide, known as water gas.

Carbon monoxide is a useful reducing agent and is used in iron smelting and other metal extractions.

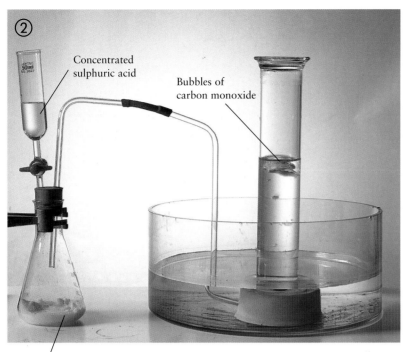

②

Concentrated
sulphuric acid

Bubbles of
carbon monoxide

Sodium methanoate
powder

Demonstration 2: reduction of carbon dioxide using a furnace

Carbon monoxide gas may be prepared by reducing carbon dioxide. This reaction only works if the reactants (carbon dioxide and carbon) are raised to a sufficiently high temperature using a laboratory furnace.

The apparatus uses a constant supply of carbon dioxide gas from Kipp's apparatus (pages 11 and 36) (①).

This is fed over granular carbon inside the furnace, where most of the carbon dioxide is reduced by red-hot carbon to carbon monoxide (④). The outlet of the furnace carries the gas through a Dreschel bottle containing sodium hydroxide solution, where any remaining carbon dioxide gas reacts to form sodium carbonate. Carbon monoxide does not react with sodium hydroxide because it is a neutral gas.

Remarks

Carbon monoxide is a toxic gas and so it is important to be sure that all of it is contained.

EQUATION: Preparation of carbon monoxide by reduction of carbon dioxide
Carbon dioxide + carbon ⇨ carbon monoxide
$CO_2(g) + C(s) ⇨ 2CO(g)$

③

Kipp's apparatus produces
a constant supply of CO_2.

Carbon furnace consisting of a
silicon tube containing charcoal
granules. This is heated by gas
jets. Heat is conserved by
surrounding the apparatus in a
ceramic liner.

The Dreschel bottle contains
sodium hydroxide to remove
any carbon dioxide gas not
reduced in the furnace.

Carbon monoxide
gas collected over
water using a gas jar
seated on a beehive
shelf in a water-filled
glass trough.

④

The furnace
being heated

Preparation of sulphur dioxide (SO$_2$)

When sulphur or sulphur-containing compounds are burned, the reaction always produces sulphur dioxide gas. Any acid also reacts with any sulphide to produce sulphur dioxide gas.

Demonstration 1: combustion of sulphur in oxygen

Sulphur dioxide can be prepared directly in a gas jar, using some powdered sulphur and a gas jar filled with oxygen (①).

A small amount of the yellow sulphur powder is first heated strongly in a combustion spoon until it begins to burn. Notice that the combustion spoon has a metal disc above it in order to protect anyone holding the spoon while the sulphur is burning. The disc also serves as a support for holding the spoon on the middle of the gas jar *(right)* and as a cover to keep the gas contained. Sulphur dioxide is heavier than air and so the gas jar is placed with the open end up.

When the sulphur is placed in the gas jar, it burns more strongly with a blue flame (②). Provided the piece of sulphur is large enough, it will continue to burn until all of the oxygen has been used up. The gas in the gas jar will then be almost entirely sulphur dioxide.

EQUATION: Burning sulphur in air
Sulphur + oxygen ⇨ sulphur dioxide
S(s) + O$_2$(g) ⇨ SO$_2$(g)

Demonstration 2: reaction of sulphuric acid with sodium sulphite

Sulphur dioxide gas can be produced by reacting dilute hydrochloric acid with sodium sulphite. This can be done in a conical flask, adding the acid from a dropper funnel, or, for smaller quantities, a side-arm boiling tube and thistle funnel can be used as shown (③).

① Gas jar of oxygen

Sulphur powder

Combustion spoon

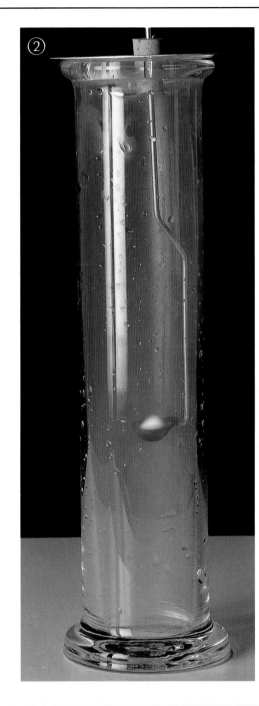

Sodium sulphite (a white powder) is first placed in the boiling tube and the stopper with the thistle funnel pushed firmly on to the tube. The sulphuric acid is then added through the thistle funnel. The reaction will take place without any external source of heat.

Sulphur dioxide is extremely soluble in water, and much of the first gas produced will therefore be absorbed into the solution of reactants. Thus it may be some while before effervescence is observed. For the same reason, sulphur dioxide cannot be collected over water, but because it is more dense than air, it should be collected by upward displacement of air (see page 13).

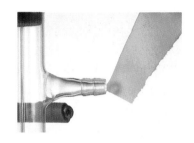

(Above) A piece of filter paper soaked in orange potassium dichromate solution will change to a blue–green colour (which may appear almost white on the filter paper) in the presence of sulphur dioxide gas. This is one test used to diagnose the presence of this powerful reducing agent.

PROPERTIES, USES AND INDUSTRIAL PRODUCTION OF SULPHUR DIOXIDE

Sulphur dioxide is a colourless, choking and poisonous gas which has a pungent smell. Sulphur dioxide is not flammable and will not support combustion.

Sulphur dioxide is over twice the density of air and will condense to its liquid state at $-10°C$. Sulphur dioxide is very soluble in water at room temperature forming an acidic solution of sulphurous acid (H_2SO_3).

Most industrial sulphur dioxide is produced during the roasting of elemental sulphur or from sulphur-containing ores during metal refining. It can also be collected from exhausts of power stations and as a byproduct of petroleum refining.

Sulphur dioxide is used widely in industry for the production of chemicals, as a bleach in foodstuffs, for laundry and for preserving alcoholic drinks. It is also used in the manufacture of paper.

As a product from the burning of fossil fuels, sulphur dioxide is an important air pollutant, contributing to acid rain.

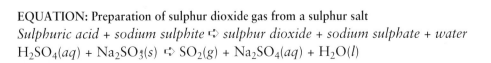

EQUATION: Preparation of sulphur dioxide gas from a sulphur salt
Sulphuric acid + sodium sulphite ⇨ sulphur dioxide + sodium sulphate + water
$H_2SO_4(aq) + Na_2SO_3(s) ⇨ SO_2(g) + Na_2SO_4(aq) + H_2O(l)$

LIQUIDS AND SOLUTIONS

Liquids

Liquids are a fluid form of matter which will assume the shape of the parts of the containers that they occupy. Although the ATOMS, IONS or MOLECULES in a liquid are sufficiently mobile to allow this, they are not so mobile as to fill the container the liquid occupies. This, and the other characteristics of liquids, determine the type of apparatus that can be used in their preparation or collection and how this might contrast with that for gases or solids.

Solutions

Liquids often occur as solutions, a mixture of more than one substance blended with another and in a liquid state. In the laboratory, solutions of known concentration are often required (see page 48). It is also common for reactions to produce solutions which then have to be separated. Techniques for both requirements are given here.

If two liquids are mixed, then usually the substance in a solution with the largest volume is called the SOLVENT while the minor constituent is called the SOLUTE. Gases are almost always solutes when dissolved in a liquid, which is the solvent. Often a solid solute is dissolved in a liquid solvent.

The way a solute behaves depends on how easily it is mixed in the solvent. Some solutes mix easily in any proportion, others will only partially dissolve. In some cases, the liquid solute does not dissolve but remains as very tiny droplets. In this case it is called an EMULSION and is a SUSPENSION rather than a true solution.

When solids are dissolved in liquids, they may be in unchanged molecules or they may break up into charged fractions known as IONS, and in this condition the solution conducts electric current and is called an ELECTROLYTE.

Simple distillation

Distillation separates liquids from solids and liquids from other liquids (see page 54). In the process, liquid turns into a vapour (it VAPORISES) before condensing as liquid again. Distillation occurs in nature in the form of the water cycle, in which rainwater falls, then evaporates from solution in the oceans or other bodies of water into the atmosphere, condenses, and falls again.

In the laboratory, distillation techniques are designed to separate out the parts of a mixture. To do this, techniques make use of the varying readiness of different liquids to vaporise. At atmospheric pressure water, for example, will form a vapour at 100°C whilst alcohol (ethanol) has a boiling point of approximately 77°C. A mixture of alcohol and water could therefore be separated by raising the temperature to just over 77°C, so that the alcohol vapour boils off. The vapours separated from the liquid during heating at different temperatures can be recondensed and collected separately.

In the simplest kind of distillation in a laboratory, such as the mixture of alcohol and water described above, only one substance vaporises, while the other components which have not vaporised remain in the original liquid. The preparation of distilled water is another example of simple distillation, where the impurities in the water are removed by boiling the original water and condensing and collecting the water vapour produced – distilled water.

Distillation equipment can contain a thermometer, which shows the temperature of the vapour (and therefore tells what the vapour is). The vapour passes down a condenser, which is surrounded by a cooling jacket. This converts the vapour back to liquid. The purified liquid, which is called the DISTILLATE, is collected in a receiving vessel.

The process uses heat to boil the liquid, and releases heat as the vapour condenses.

Fractional distillation

This is a technique used to separate a mixture of liquids that boil at different temperatures (see page 56). It is a more advanced form of simple distillation. Fractional distillation is used widely in industry, for example, as a method for separating crude oil.

When a mixture of two or more liquids is boiled, the vapour will contain molecules of all the substances and so it is important to design an apparatus that collects the various fractions (pure liquids) as they cool. To achieve this, the mixture to be separated is placed in a flask and boiled. It is then boiled and passed into a fractionating column which allows vapour to condense and be reboiled by the heat from other vapours as it, in turn, condenses. As a result of the repeated distillation in the column, the fraction with the lowest boiling point reaches the top of

Preparation of distilled water: a simple distillation

You will find a powered laboratory apparatus for making distilled water in most laboratories. It is an example of simple distillation, designed to remove the naturally dissolved substances from the water. Tap water is boiled and the water vapour (steam) produced is passed over a large surface area of coiled tubing that is cooled using cold tap water. The water vapour condenses and is drained off and collected as distilled water.

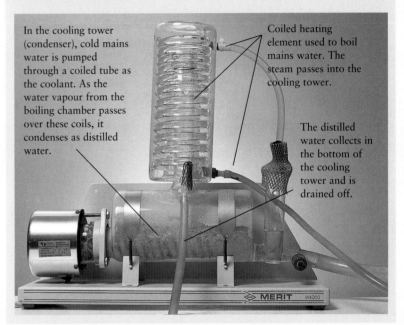

In the cooling tower (condenser), cold mains water is pumped through a coiled tube as the coolant. As the water vapour from the boiling chamber passes over these coils, it condenses as distilled water.

Coiled heating element used to boil mains water. The steam passes into the cooling tower.

The distilled water collects in the bottom of the cooling tower and is drained off.

the column first. Each fraction can be collected separately.

Steam distillation

Steam distillation is used to distil liquids such as aniline that do not dissolve in water. The solution is placed in a flask with water, and steam is passed through the flask. The vapour of the VOLATILE liquid is carried with the steam and condenses in the receiving vessel as a separate layer from the water.

Separating immiscible liquids using a separating funnel

A separating funnel is a useful piece of apparatus for separating two solutions that do not mix (are IMMISCIBLE). Essentially, the easiest way to separate two immiscible liquids is to drain the more dense liquid first. The less dense liquid can then be drained afterwards.

Demonstration: separation of purple potassium permanganate from colourless carbon tetrachloride

The key to successful separation is to use a tear-drop shape separating funnel. This is designed so that, towards the tap, the cross-sectional area is progressively smaller. This means that, while a large amount of liquid can be held in the funnel, the narrow neck makes it easier to see the point at which all of the first liquid has been drained off.

The two liquids are poured into the separating funnel (①). The clear carbon tetrachloride is more dense than the purple potassium permanganate solution and so it sinks to the bottom of the funnel.

The tap is turned and the carbon tetrachloride run out into a beaker (②). When the carbon tetrachloride has almost flowed out, the tap is partly closed, to reduce the rate at which liquid flows out. The key to successful separation is to be able to close the tap accurately and speedily, so that neither liquid

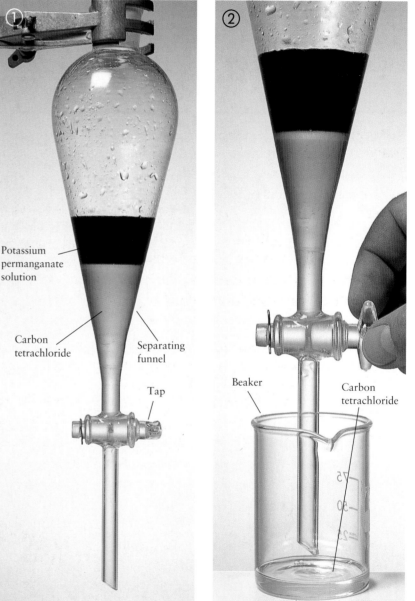

Potassium permanganate solution

Carbon tetrachloride

Separating funnel

Tap

Beaker

Carbon tetrachloride

is contaminated with small amounts of
the other. Thus, as the last few drops
of carbon tetrachloride are run out,
the glass tap is studied closely (③).

The advantage of the glass tap is that
you can see the liquid inside the tap. The
aim is to close the tap fully when the last
of the carbon tetrachloride is leaving the
tap, and the less dense liquid is just
entering it. You can see this critical
point in the picture (④).

Now that the carbon tetrachloride
has been separated, it can be taken
away and the tap then opened partially
to allow a small amount of the potassium
permanganate solution to flow out and
flush any carbon tetrachloride out of
the tap.

The tap can now be opened wide and
the rest of the potassium permanganate
solution can be poured into a separate
beaker.

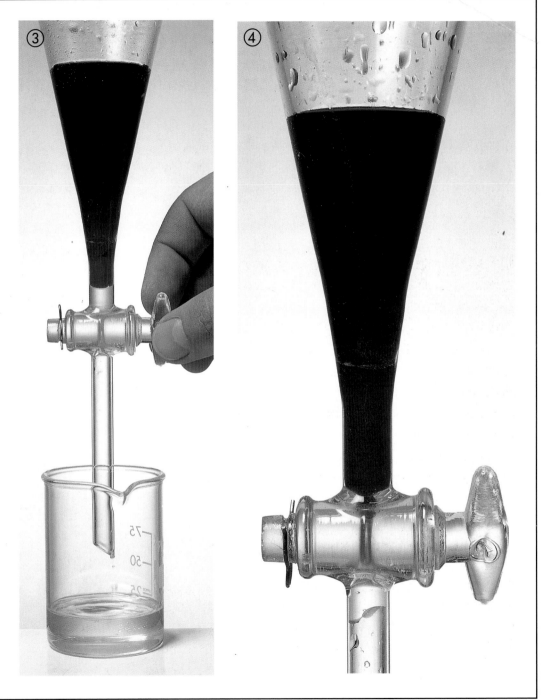

Preparing a solution of known concentration

If you are performing a QUANTITATIVE experiment, you will need to know the CONCENTRATION of any solutions you use. In this demonstration, you can see the steps needed to make a solution of known concentration. The solution is prepared as grams of solid per litre of solution.

Demonstration: making a solution containing 500g/l potassium permanganate

The potassium permanganate first has to be weighed out using an electronic balance. As the concentration of the solution is to be 500g per litre, and the measuring flask used holds 100ml (= 0·12), then 50g of potassium permanganate will be required. Add the solid to a beaker, first TARING (allowing for) the mass of the beaker (①).

A small amount of distilled water is added to the beaker using a wash bottle (②). The solution is stirred to ensure that all the potassium permanganate has dissolved. It is important not to add too much distilled water at this stage (③).

The solution is then poured into a (standard) measuring flask using the same stirring rod and a small funnel, ensuring that none of the solution is spilled (④). The wash bottle is used again to wash any residue from the beaker, the stirring rod and the funnel into the flask (⑤ & ⑥).

Next, more distilled water is added to bring the level of the bottom of the MENISCUS to the etched line on the flask (⑦).

The stopper is then placed on the flask and the flask shaken to ensure an even distribution of potassium permanganate in the solution (⑧).

When the flask is stood upright again, the level of solution will probably be slightly below the line on the neck of the flask (⑨). This is because a small amount of solution will now be adhering to the neck of the flask and the stopper. However, this will not affect the *concentration* of the sample.

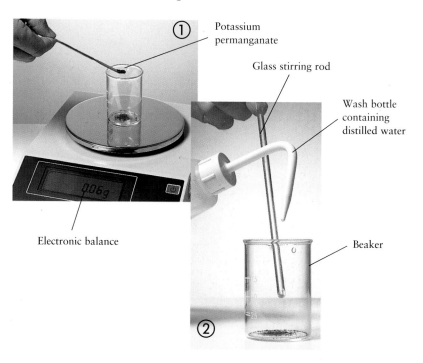

① Potassium permanganate

Glass stirring rod

Wash bottle containing distilled water

Electronic balance

Beaker

②

48

③

Glass funnel

Measuring flask

Stopper

④

⑤

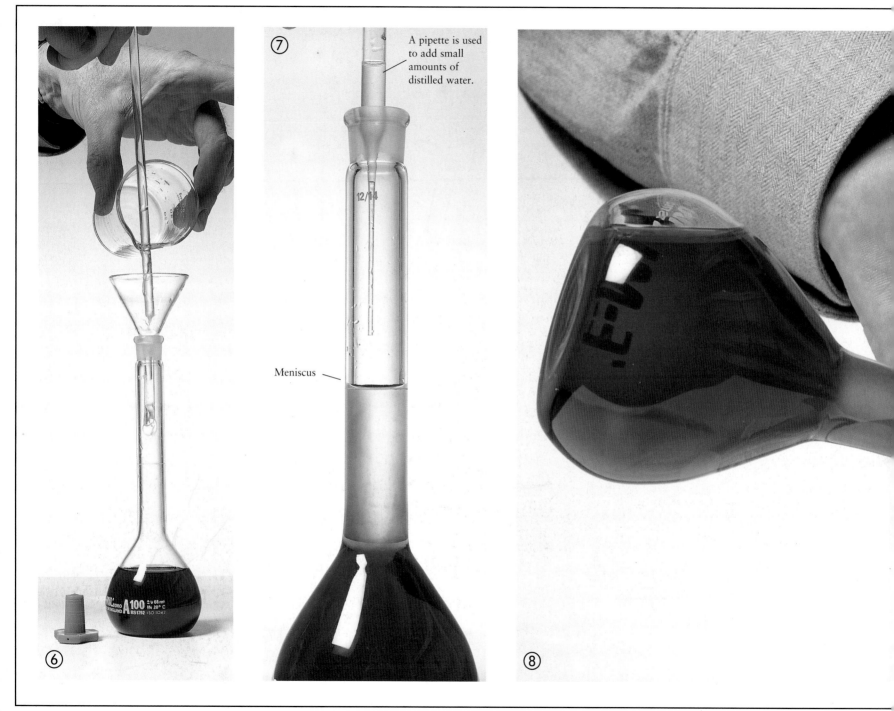

⑥

⑦ A pipette is used to add small amounts of distilled water.

12/14

Meniscus

⑧

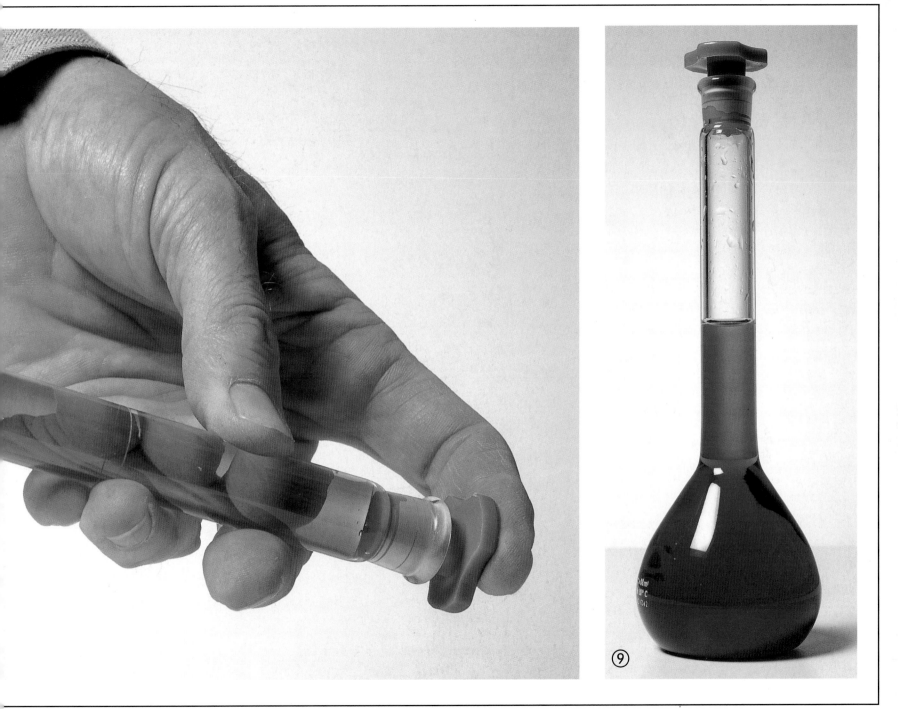

Dissolving gases in liquids

Some gases are soluble in water and will create ACIDIC or ALKALINE solutions. For example, hydrogen chloride gas is readily soluble in water and will produce hydrochloric acid. Similarly, nitrogen dioxide will dissolve to form nitric acid, and sulphur dioxide will dissolve to produce sulphurous acid. The only common gas to produce an alkaline gas, however, is ammonia.

Demonstration 1: dissolving hydrogen chloride gas in water

To dissolve a gas in a liquid, the gas must be brought into close contact with the liquid. If a delivery tube is simply placed in the liquid and the gas allowed to bubble up, much of the gas will be lost to the air. The purpose of the inverted funnel is to provide a large surface area for the gas to be in contact with the liquid and at the same time minimise the loss of gas to the air.

The hydrogen chloride is prepared by the method shown on page 32. It is then led through a delivery tube to the inverted funnel. It is important that the rim of the funnel is below the surface of the water at all times (①). In this case, the rate of reaction is controlled by the rate at which sulphuric acid is added.

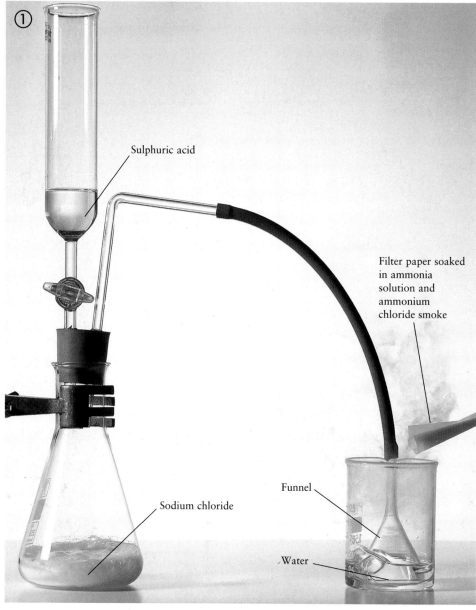

①

Sulphuric acid

Filter paper soaked in ammonia solution and ammonium chloride smoke

Sodium chloride

Funnel

Water

Demonstration 2: dissolving ammonia in water

Ammonia is prepared by the method shown on page 24. It is then led through a delivery tube to the inverted funnel. As in the previous demonstration, it is important that the rim of the funnel is below the surface of the water at all times (②). In this case, the rate of reaction is controlled by the amount of heating.

Remarks

Notice that only a small amount of water is being used. The more water used, the more dilute the acid or alkali, or the more gas that would have to be prepared in order to produce a desired level of concentration.

If the rate of gas production is too high, gas will bubble from under the funnel. Although this will not stop gas dissolving in the water, it is wasteful of gas. To prevent this, the reaction can be slowed down by reducing the rate of addition of reactants or by reducing the amount of heat as appropriate.

Some gases are extremely soluble in water and, as a result, the gas can be sucked out of the delivery tube faster than new gas is formed, creating a vacuum in the flask. If a simple delivery tube were used, there would be a danger of the water being sucked back up the delivery tube into the flask. This could stop the reaction, and in some circumstances be dangerous. The use of an inverted funnel prevents this problem.

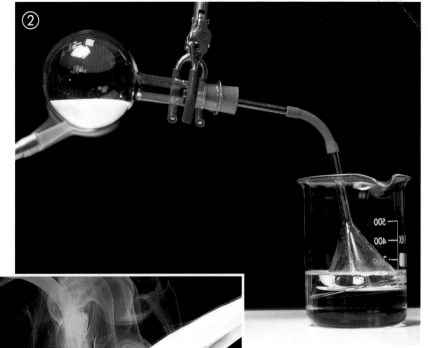

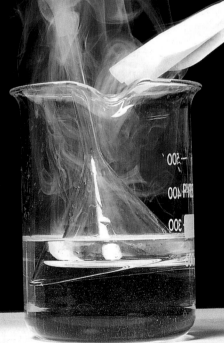

(*Left*) Ammonia is extremely soluble in water and will form ammonia solution.

Despite its solubility, some ammonia gas remains undissolved and this is detected using filter paper soaked in hydrochloric acid. The white smoke produced is ammonium chloride.

Simple distillation

Simple distillation separates a SOLVENT from a SOLUTION by making use of the boiling point of the solvent.

Demonstration: distillation of ethanoic acid

The distillation of ethanoic acid ($CH_3 COOH$, vinegar) solution (①) uses a flask coupled to a LIEBIG CONDENSER. A Liebig condenser is a convenient way of making a vapour condense into a liquid. It consists of a water jacket around a central delivery tube. Cold tap water is passed through the water jacket. The cold water removes heat from the central delivery tube,

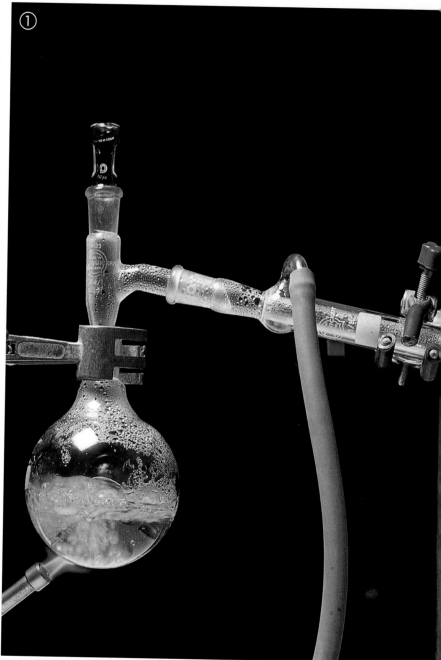

①

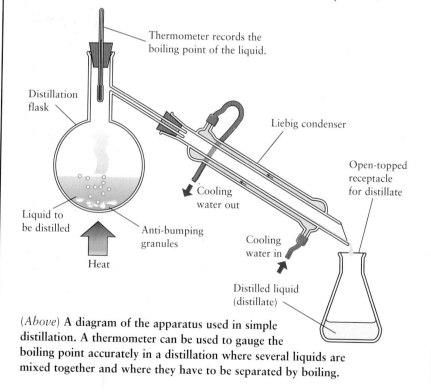

Thermometer records the boiling point of the liquid.

Distillation flask

Liebig condenser

Open-topped receptacle for distillate

Liquid to be distilled

Cooling water out

Anti-bumping granules

Cooling water in

Heat

Distilled liquid (distillate)

(*Above*) A diagram of the apparatus used in simple distillation. A thermometer can be used to gauge the boiling point accurately in a distillation where several liquids are mixed together and where they have to be separated by boiling.

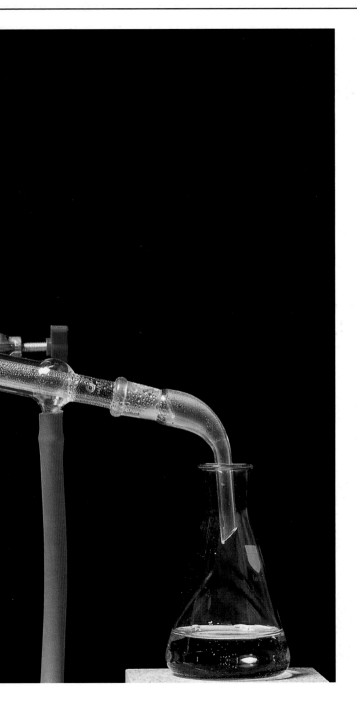

causing the vapour in the tube to condense to a liquid. The condensed liquid, known as the distillate, is collected.

For this demonstration, ethanoic acid is produced by reacting ethanol with acidified potassium dichromate. This mixture is heated and, as the reaction progresses, the solution becomes green. The liquid mixture is then separated using simple distillation as shown here.

Some inert anti-bumping granules are first added to the flask containing the liquid to be distilled. In the case of simple distillation, there is no need to fit a thermometer unless the boiling point of the vapour is of interest. The liquid is then heated until it boils. The anti-bumping granules ensure smooth boiling without excessive formation of large bubbles. The vapour passes through the Liebig condenser, cools to a liquid state, and is collected in the conical flask.

Remarks

The same method cannot be used for separating mixtures of a number of liquids. In this case, a fractionating column is required as shown in the demonstration on page 56.

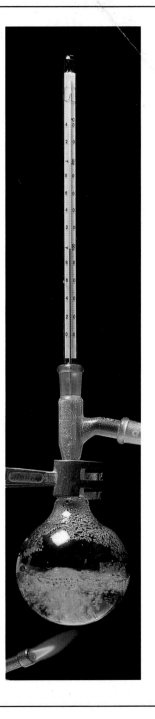

Fractional distillation

Fractional distillation is a technique used to separate complex mixtures, many of which are volatile. It is most commonly used to separate the many fractions (parts of the mixture) in petroleum.

Demonstration 1: fractional distillation of crude oil

Petroleum contains liquids, solids and dissolved gases. These can each be separated by progressive heating of the mixture. If the boiling point of each fraction is known, then the temperature in the distillation flask can be raised in stages until the temperature of the column allows one component to reach the top of the column. The thermometer will then record its boiling point. The vapour produced can then be collected.

Fractional distillation can only be done with a specialised piece of apparatus called a FRACTIONATING COLUMN ①. This might be a column filled with beads or, as is shown here, a glass spiral that is placed above the heated liquid.

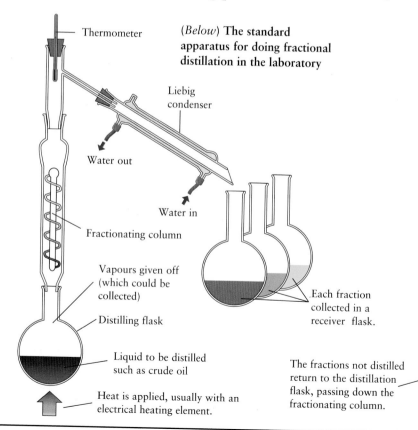

Thermometer

(*Below*) **The standard apparatus for doing fractional distillation in the laboratory**

Liebig condenser

Water out

Fractionating column

Vapours given off (which could be collected)

Distilling flask

Liquid to be distilled such as crude oil

Heat is applied, usually with an electrical heating element.

Water in

Each fraction collected in a receiver flask.

The fractions not distilled return to the distillation flask, passing down the fractionating column.

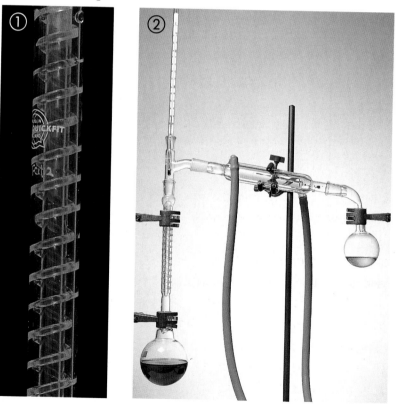

The mixture is heated, using a heating element, just sufficiently to make the most volatile fraction pass through the column and be condensed and collected. Any heavier vapours that have also evaporated, cool before they reach the top of the column, condense and pass back down to the original liquid (②).

The temperature is then raised in order to collect the next most volatile fraction (③). At each stage the chosen temperature is kept constant by observing the thermometer above the fractionating column (④) and varying the heat applied to the mixture.

The original oil has been reduced in volume by the distillation, but it has also darkened as the heavier residues are left behind.

A 'light' fraction

A 'heavy' fraction

Remarks

The more volatile fractions that are collected at the lower temperatures are called 'light fractions' (⑤). The higher the temperature that the crude oil is heated to, the darker the colour of the fraction that is collected. Those less volatile fractions collected at the higher temperatures are called 'heavy fractions'. In all cases, the fractions are noticeably lighter in colour when compared to the original mixture, which itself gets progressively darker with heating.

INDUSTRIAL USE OF FRACTIONAL DISTILLATION OF CRUDE OIL

Crude oil is refined industrially using fractional distillation in a fractionating column, which may be some 60m tall. Whereas in a laboratory batches are collected for varying temperatures, the industrial fractional distillation must be continuous and the aim is to extract a wide range of products at the same time. The table below shows the main fractions that are obtained by industrial fractional distillation, the temperatures at which they boil and their uses.

Fraction	Boiling point range/°C	Uses
Refinery gas	Up to 40	Gases for cookers, liquefied petroleum gas (LPG)
Petrol	40–140	Fuel for vehicles, chemicals
Naphtha	140–180	Raw material for chemicals and plastics
Paraffin	180–250	Aircraft fuel, heating and raw material for chemicals
Light gas oil	250–300	Diesel fuel for trains and lorries, raw material for chemicals, plastics
Heavy gas oil	300–340	Fuel for boilers in ships, factories and heating
Bitumen	Above 340	Surface and sealant for roads and roofing

Titration

TITRATION is a QUANTITATIVE way of adding one reactant to another until some final point is reached, for example, preparing a soluble salt from an acid and a soluble base, or finding out the degree of water hardness by using a soap solution.

Demonstration: calculating the volume of an acid that reacts with a known volume of an alkaline solution to produce a salt

A titration occurs when an acid is added to a base in such a proportion that a neutral product (a salt) is produced. Because this is a quantitative method, precautions have to be taken to make sure that the measurements are accurate.

The apparatus used is shown in the diagram (①). The first stage is to fill the BURETTE, including the space (known as the dead space) below the tap, by gradually releasing liquid out of the base of the burette until the dead space has been filled (② & ③). If desired, more liquid can then be run out of the burette to bring the level of the MENISCUS in the burette to the zero mark (④), or the starting level of the liquid can simply be read from the graduated tube.

The important part of a titration is the end point, when exact amounts of reactants have combined. It is therefore critical to the success of the method that this end point is arrived at with great accuracy.

To show this most clearly, this demonstration uses a small amount of acid solution in a Petri dish, and an alkali in the burette, but if larger quantities are to be titrated, then the acid would be in a flask. Similarly, the acid could be in the burette and the alkali in the flask (chosen so that it can be shaken without spillage).

The end point can be determined using a colour indicator, as shown here, or by using a pH meter, in

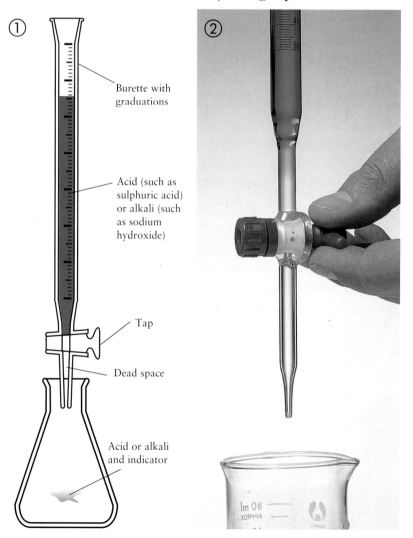

① Burette with graduations

Acid (such as sulphuric acid) or alkali (such as sodium hydroxide)

Tap

Dead space

Acid or alkali and indicator

②

which case the titration is continued until the meter shows a NEUTRAL pH.

In this demonstration, phenolphthalein was used as the indicator and was added to the acid solution in the Petri dish. Phenolphthalein turns pink when alkaline (above 7.0 on the pH scale). Initially the phenolphthalein in the acidic solution remains colourless (⑤, see page 60).

To see how the titration works, a few drops of alkali from the burette are dripped into the solution in the dish. For a short time, the effect of the alkali is to trigger a colour response in the indicator. A flash of pink colour is seen where the drops enter the acid, but quickly disappear (⑥).

Over a few minutes, with the burette being allowed to drip slowly, most of the acid is neutralised and the pink flash of colour lasts longer and becomes more extensive (⑦). However, this pink patch can be dispersed easily with stirring (⑧).

As the end point is reached, the pink colour remains as a patch that does not disperse easily. When this stage is reached, the drop rate needs to be reduced. As more alkali is added, so the pink-coloured patch becomes more difficult to disperse (⑨) until the end point is finally reached when the pink colour can no longer be dispersed by stirring (⑩). It may only require one drop to cause this transition from colourless to permanently pink. The acid has now been neutralised.

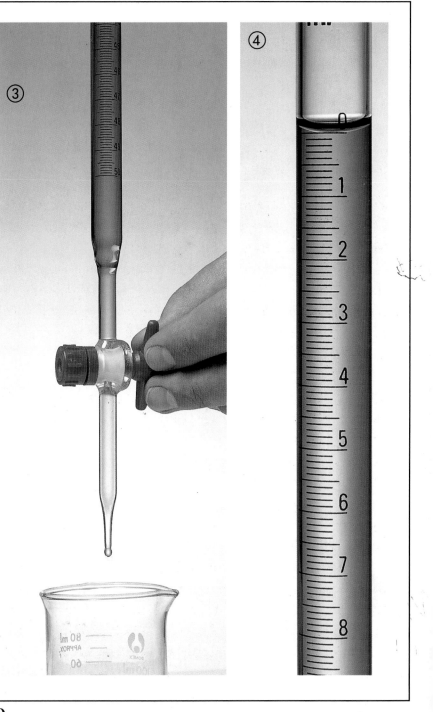

③   ④

⑤ Phenolphthalein indicator. This indicator is colourless when acid but turns pink when the solution becomes alkaline.

⑥ Where the solution is alkaline, the indicator turns pink. However, before the end point is reached, the pink spot can be dispersed by stirring (see ⑦ and ⑧).

⑦

⑧ Glass rod is used for stirring.

⑨ As the end point is reached, it becomes more difficult to disperse the colour but, until the end point is reached, the solution goes back to being colourless.

⑩ When the indicator remains pink on stirring, the end point has been reached.

SOLIDS AND PRECIPITATES

A solid is a rigid form of matter that maintains its shape whatever container it is placed in. The particles that make up a solid STATE OF MATTER are not free to move about as they are in the gas or liquid states.

The majority of natural substances are solids at normal temperatures and pressure. The fact that a solid is rigid does not, of course, mean that it is unreactive. In fact, many of the reactants in a chemistry laboratory are found as solids, often as powders, granules, chippings or turnings.

A precipitate is a collection of solid particles that separate from a liquid and settle out as a result of a physical or chemical change.

It is often very convenient to be able to cause precipitation to occur as a means of preparing substances. The precipitate can then usually be collected by filtration (see page 62), washed, dried, and weighed. A small sample of a liquid and a solid may also be separated using a centrifuge as shown on this page. If the precipitate is a mixture, then further separation may be necessary. Precipitation is the basis of an important method in chemistry called GRAVIMETRIC ANALYSIS.

There are many forms of precipitate. Some precipitates contain large amounts of water and form a jelly-like substance, known as a GELATINOUS PRECIPITATE. Other precipitates group together into a solid mass. This is called COAGULATION or FLOCCULATION. These precipitates are granular.

(Left, below and right) **A centrifuge uses the increased gravitational force caused by rapid rotation to separate mixtures.**

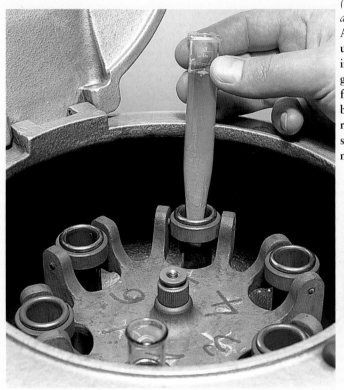

Separating a precipitate from a solution by filtration

FILTRATION is one of the most fundamental techniques used for separating solids and liquids. It is used most easily when there is a pure solid to be separated from a solution.

Demonstration 1: filtration of a yellow precipitate of lead iodide using gravity

The apparatus consists of a conical flask, a small glass filter funnel and a larger disc of filter paper which is folded in such a way as to fit into the funnel (① & ②). The funnel is placed in the neck of the flask and the filter paper placed in the funnel. Wetting the filter paper with distilled water will help the filter paper sit in the funnel. The size of the filter paper is not important and a disc can be used that is larger than the funnel, but in such a case it is vital to make sure that the filter paper is not filled above the level of the top of the funnel (③).

To make sure all of the contents of the boiling tube containing the precipitate of lead iodide go into the

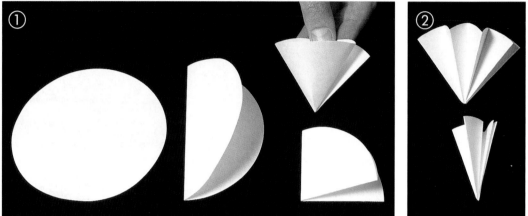

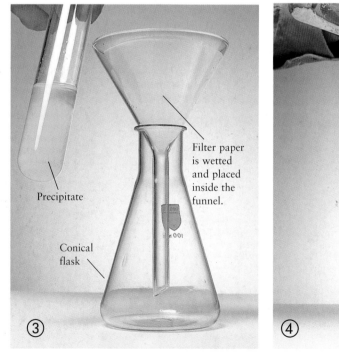

Precipitate

Conical flask

③

Filter paper is wetted and placed inside the funnel.

④

funnel, the contents are stirred vigorously before pouring and then poured all at once using a glass rod as a guide to prevent splashing during pouring (④).

Any remaining precipitate (⑤) is then washed out of the tube using a wash bottle filled with distilled water, and the filtrate (the solution) is washed through the filter paper using distilled water (⑥). It is important to make sure that all of the filtrate is washed through by using enough distilled water.

The filter paper is then removed from the funnel, opened out with the precipitate upwards and stood in

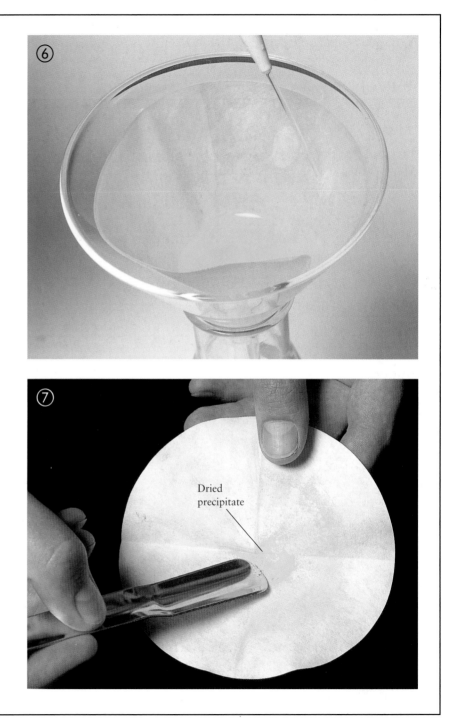

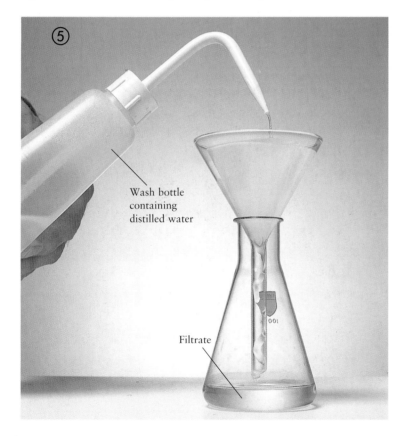

Wash bottle containing distilled water

Filtrate

Dried precipitate

a dust-free place until it is dried (⑦, see page 63). The precipitate is then removed from the filter paper by first flexing the paper to break the precipitate from the paper and then gently tapping the paper to shake off the precipitate.

Demonstration 2: filtration of brick-red silver chromate(I) using a suction pump

A suction pump is used to speed up the process of filtration. Pumped filtration uses two special pieces of equipment: a BÜCHNER FUNNEL and a BÜCHNER FLASK, both designed to work under suction.

A Büchner flask is a thick-walled flask designed to withstand pressure. A Büchner funnel (made, in this case, of white plastic) is designed similarly to withstand the suction produced by a pump. It consists of a straight-walled funnel containing a disc of paper which rests on a deck of plastic containing an array of small holes.

A disc of dry filter paper is placed on the deck (⑧) and then wetted thoroughly so that, when the suction is applied, the wet filter paper will be pulled firmly down on the deck. The funnel is seated firmly on the flask and the flask is connected to a pump.

Once the filter paper is firmly in place, the precipitate and solution from the boiling tube are poured into the funnel down a glass rod to prevent splashing that might occur if the contents were simply poured in undirected (⑨).

The contents of the tube and the rod are now washed clean with distilled water, making sure that all materials go into the funnel (⑩).

Suction is applied using a water pump connected to the flask via its side arm. As the suction builds up in the flask, the solution collects at the bottom of the funnel and the precipitate remains on the filter paper. To make sure there is no solution left on the filter paper, distilled water is poured on to the paper and precipitate during the pumping process (⑪). The larger volume of liquid in the flask compared with the boiling tube is caused by the amount of distilled water that is used in washing the tube and the precipitate. The orange solution in the flask is excess potassium chromate(I).

The filter paper is carefully picked out of the funnel (⑫) and the disc allowed to dry in air in a dust-free place (⑬). When it is dry, the filter paper is flexed gently and tapped with a rod to separate the precipitate from the filter paper (⑭).

Remarks

Notice that the washing stage is very important for any quantitative technique. (Note that some solutions will not be in water as the solvent and so in such cases an alternative 'washing' liquid may have to be used.)

Once the filtration is complete, the precipitate must be separated carefully from the filter paper. The solid on the filter paper is then left to dry, it is not artificially dried using a heater as this may disturb the precipitation. The solid is tipped off the filter paper, not scraped because scraping will also remove some cellulose paper fibres and contaminate the filtered solid.

Filter paper

Büchner funnel

Büchner flask is connected to a suction pump by a length of tubing.

Wash bottle containing distilled water

Solution with silver chromate precipitate

Filtrate

Silver chromate precipitate

⑧ ⑨ ⑩ ⑪ ⑫ ⑬ ⑭

MASTER GLOSSARY

absolute zero: the lowest possible temperature (−273.15°C).

absorption: the process by which a substance is soaked up. *See:* adsorption.

acid: a substance that can give a proton to another substance. Acids are compounds, containing hydrogen, that can attack and dissolve many substances. Acids are described as weak or strong, dilute or concentrated, mineral or organic. *Example:* hydrochloric acid (HCl). An acid in water can react with a base to form a salt and water.

acidic solution: a solution with a pH lower than 7.

acidity: a general term for the strength of an acid in a solution.

acid radical: the negative ion left behind when an acid loses a hydrogen ion. *Example:* Cl⁻ in hydrochloric acid (HCl).

acid salt: An ACID SALT contains at least one hydrogen ion and can behave as an acid in chemical reactions. Acid salts are produced under conditions that do not allow complete neutralisation of the acid. For example, sulphuric acid may react with a sodium compound to produce a normal sodium salt, sodium sulphate (Na_2SO_4), or it may retain some of the hydrogen, in which case it becomes the salt sodium hydrogen sulphate ($NaHSO_4$).

actinide series or actinide metals: a series of 15 similar radioactive elements between actinium and lawrencium. They are transition metals.

activated charcoal: a form of carbon, made up of tiny crystals of graphite, which is made by heating organic matter in the absence of air. It is then processed further to increase its pore space and therefore its surface area. Its surface area is about 2000 m^2/g. Activated charcoal readily adsorbs many gases and it is therefore widely used as a filter, for example, in gas masks.

activation energy: the energy required to make a reaction occur. The greater the activation energy of a reaction, the more its reaction rate depends on temperature. The activation energy of a reaction is useful because, if the rate of reaction is known at one temperature (for example, 100°C) then the activation energy can be used to calculate the rate of reaction at another temperature (for example, 400°C) without actually doing the experiment.

adsorption: the process by which a surface adsorbs a substance. The substances involved are not chemically combined and can be separated. *Example:* the adsorption properties of activated charcoal. *See:* absorption.

alchemy: the traditional 'art' of working with chemicals that prevailed through the Middle Ages. One of the main challenges for alchemists was to make gold from lead. Alchemy faded away as scientific chemistry was developed in the 17th century.

alcohol: an organic compound which contains a hydroxyl (OH) group. *Example:* ethanol (CH_3CH_2OH), also known as ethyl alcohol or grain alcohol.

alkali/alkaline: a base in (aqueous) solution. Alkalis react with, or neutralise, hydrogen ions in acids and have a pH greater than 7.0 because they contain relatively few hydrogen ions. *Example:* aqueous sodium hydroxide (NaOH).

alkali metals: a member of Group 1 of the Periodic Table. *Example:* sodium.

alkaline cell (or battery): a dry cell in which the electrolyte contains sodium or potassium hydroxide.

alkaline earth metal: a member of Group 2 of the Periodic Table. *Example:* calcium.

alkane: a hydrocarbon with no carbon-to-carbon multiple bonds. *Example:* ethane, C_2H_6.

alkene: a hydrocarbon with at least one carbon-to-carbon double bond. *Example:* ethene, C_2H_4.

alkyne: a hydrocarbon with at least one carbon-to-carbon triple bond. *Example:* ethyne, C_2H_2.

allotropes: alternative forms of an element that differ in the way the atoms are linked. *Example:* white and red phosphorus.

alloy: a mixture of a metal and various other elements. *Example:* brass is an alloy of copper and zinc.

amalgam: a liquid alloy of mercury with another metal.

amorphous: a solid in which the atoms are not arranged regularly (i.e. glassy). Compare crystalline.

amphoteric: a metal that will react with both acids and alkalis. *Example:* aluminium metal.

anhydrous: lacking water; water has been removed, for example, by heating. Many hydrated salts are crystalline. (Opposite of anhydrous is hydrous or hydrated.) *Example:* copper(II) sulphate can be anhydrous ($CuSO_4$) or hydrated ($CuSO_4 \cdot 5H_2O$).

anion: a negatively charged atom or group of atoms. *Examples:* chloride ion (Cl⁻), hydroxide ion (OH⁻).

anode: the electrode at which oxidation occurs; the negative terminal of a battery or the positive electrode of an electrolysis cell.

anodising: a process that uses the effect of electrolysis to make a surface corrosion resistant. *Example:* anodised aluminium.

antacid: a common name for any compound that reacts with stomach acid to neutralise it. *Example:* sodium hydrogen carbonate, also known as sodium bicarbonate.

anti-bumping granules: small glass or ceramic beads, designed to promote boiling without the development of large gas bubbles.

antioxidant: a substance that reacts rapidly with radicals thereby preventing oxidation of some other substance.

approximate relative atomic mass: *See:* relative atomic mass.

aqueous: a solution in which the solvent is water. Usually used as 'aqueous solution'. *Example:* aqueous solution of sodium hydroxide (NaOH(*aq*)).

aromatic hydrocarbons: compounds of carbon that have the benzene ring as part of their structure. *Examples:* benzene (C_6H_6), naphthalene ($C_{10}H_8$). They are known as aromatic because of the strong pungent smell given off by benzene.

atmospheric pressure: the pressure exerted by the gases in the air. Units of measurement are kilopascals (kPa), atmospheres (atm), millimetres of mercury (mm Hg) and Torr. Standard atmospheric pressure is 100 kPa, 1atm, 760 mm Hg or 760 Torr.

atom: the smallest particle of an element; a nucleus and its surrounding electrons.

atomic mass: the mass of an atom measured in atomic mass units (amu). An atomic mass unit is equal to one-twelfth of the atom of carbon-12. Atomic mass is now more generally used instead of atomic weight. *Example:* the atomic mass of chlorine is about 35 amu. *See:* atomic weight, relative atomic mass.

atomic number: also known as proton number. The number of electrons or the number of protons in an atom. *Example:* the atomic number of gold is 79 and for carbon it is 4.

atomic structure: the nucleus and the arrangement of electrons around the nucleus of an atom.

atomic weight: a common term used to mean the average molar mass of an element. This is the mass per mole of atoms. *Example:* the atomic weight of chlorine is about 35 g/mol. *See:* atomic mass, mole.

base: a substance that can accept a proton from another substance. *Example:* aqueous ammonia ($NH_3(aq)$). A base can react with an acid in water to form a salt and water.

basic salt: a salt that contains at least one hydroxide ion. The hydroxide ion can then behave as a base in chemical reactions. *Example:* the reaction of hydrochloric acid (HCl) with the base, aluminium hydroxide ($Al(OH)_3$) can form two basic salts, $Al(OH)_2Cl$ and $Al(OH)Cl_2$.

battery: a number of electrochemical cells placed in series.

bauxite: a hydrated impure oxide of aluminium ($Al_2O_3 \cdot xH_2O$, with the amount of water x being variable). It is the main ore used to obtain aluminium metal. The reddish-brown colour of bauxite is mainly caused by the iron oxide impurities it contains.

beehive shelf: an inverted earthenware bowl with a hole in the upper surface and a slot in the rim. Traditionally, the earthenware was brown and looked similar to a beehive, hence its name. A delivery tube passes through the slot and a gas jar is placed over the hole. This provides a convenient way to collect gas over water in a pneumatic trough.

bell jar: a tall glass jar with an open bottom and a wide, stoppered neck that is used in conjunction with a beehive shelf and a pneumatic trough in some experiments involving gases. The name derives from historic versions of the apparatus, which resembled a bell in shape.

blast furnace: a tall furnace charged with a mixture of iron ore, coke and limestone and used for the refining of iron metal. The name comes from the strong blast of air introduced during smelting.

bleach: a substance that removes colour in stains on materials, either by oxidising or reducing the staining compound. *Example:* sulphur dioxide (SO_2).

block: one of the main divisions of the Periodic Table. Blocks are named for the outermost, occupied electron shell of an element. *Example:* The Transition Metals all belong to the d-block.

boiling point: the temperature at which a liquid boils, changing from a liquid to a gas. Boiling points change with atmospheric pressure. *Example:* The boiling point of pure water at standard atmospheric pressure is 100 °C.

boiling tube: A thin glass tube closed at one end and used for chemical tests, etc. The composition and thickness of the glass is such that it cannot sustain very high temperatures and is intended for heating liquids to boiling point. *See:* side-arm boiling tube, test tube.

bond: chemical bonding is either a transfer or sharing of electrons by two or more atoms. There are a number of types of chemical bond, some very strong (such as covalent and ionic bonds), others weak (such as hydrogen bonds). Chemical bonds form because the linked molecule is more stable than the unlinked atoms from which it formed. *Example:* the hydrogen molecule (H_2) is more stable than single atoms of hydrogen, which is why hydrogen gas is always found as molecules of two hydrogen atoms.

Boyle's Law: at constant temperature, and for a given mass of gas, the volume of the gas (V) is inversely proportional to pressure that builds up (P): $P \propto 1/V$.

brine: a solution of salt (sodium chloride, NaCl) in water.

Büchner flask: a thick-walled side-arm flask designed to withstand the changes in pressure that occur when the flask is connected to a suction pump.

Büchner funnel: a special design of plastic or ceramic funnel which has a flat stage on which a filter paper can be placed. It is intended for use under suction with a Büchner flask.

buffer (solution): a mixture of substances in solution that resists a change in the acidity or alkalinity of the solution when small amounts of an acid or alkali are added.

burette: a long, graduated glass tube with a tap at one end. A burette is used vertically, with the tap lowermost. Its main use is as a reservoir for a chemical during titration.

burn: a combustion reaction in which a flame is produced. A flame occurs where *gases* combust and release heat and light. At least two gases are therefore required if there is to be a flame. *Example:* methane gas (CH_4) burns in oxygen gas (O_2) to produce carbon dioxide (CO_2) and water (H_2O) and give out heat and light.

calorimeter: an insulated container designed to prevent heat gain or loss with the environment and thus allow changes of temperature within reacting chemicals to be measured accurately. It is named after the old unit of heat, the calorie.

capillary: a very small diameter (glass) tube. Capillary tubing has a small enough diameter to allow surface tension effects to retain water within the tube.

capillary action: the tendency for a liquid to be sucked into small spaces, such as between objects and through narrow-pore tubes. The force to do this comes from surface tension.

carbohydrate: a compound containing only carbon, hydrogen and oxygen. Carbohydrates have the formula $C_n(H_2O)_n$, where n is variable. *Example:* glucose ($C_6H_{12}O_6$).

carbonate: a salt of carbonic acid. Carbonate ions have the chemical formula CO_3^{2-}. *Examples:* calcium carbonate $CaCO_3$ and sodium carbonate Na_2CO_3.

catalyst: a substance that speeds up a chemical reaction, but itself remains unaltered at the end of the reaction. *Example:* copper in the reaction of hydrochloric acid with zinc.

catalytic converter: a device incorporated into some exhaust systems. The catalytic converter contains a framework and/or granules with a very large surface area and coated with catalysts that convert the pollutant gases passing over them into harmless products.

cathode: the electrode at which reduction occurs; the positive terminal of a battery or the negative electrode of an electrolysis cell.

cathodic protection: the technique of protecting a metal object by connecting it to a more readily oxidisable metal. The metal object being protected is made into the cathode of a cell. *Example:* iron can be protected by coupling it with magnesium. Iron forms the cathode and magnesium the anode.

cation: a positively charged ion. *Examples:* calcium ion (Ca^{2+}), ammonium ion (NH_4^+).

caustic: a substance that can cause burns if it touches the skin. *Example:* Sodium hydroxide, caustic soda (NaOH).

cell: a vessel containing two electrodes and an electrolyte that can act as an electrical conductor.

Celsius scale (°C): a temperature scale on which the freezing point of water is at 0 degrees and the normal boiling point at standard atmospheric pressure is 100 degrees.

centrifuge: an instrument for spinning small samples very rapidly. The fast spin causes the components of a mixture that have a different density to separate. This has the same effect as filtration.

ceramic: a material based on clay minerals which has been heated so that it has chemically hardened.

chalcogens: the members of Group 6 of the Periodic Table: oxygen, sulphur, selenium and tellurium. The word comes from the Greek meaning 'brass giver', because all these elements are found in copper ores, and copper is the most important metal in making brass.

change of state: a change between two of the three states of matter, solid, liquid and gas. *Example:* when water evaporates it changes from a liquid to a gaseous state.

Charles's Law: the volume (V) of a given mass of gas at constant pressure is directly proportional to its absolute temperature (T): $V \propto T$.

chromatography: a separation technique using the ability of surfaces to adsorb substances with different strengths. The substances with the least adherence to the surface move faster and leave behind those that adhere more strongly.

coagulation: a term describing the tendency of small particles to stick together in clumps.

coherent: meaning that a substance holds together or sticks together well, and without holes or other defects. *Example:* Aluminium appears unreactive because, as soon as new metal is exposed to air, it forms a very complete oxide coating, which then stops further reaction occurring.

coinage metals: the elements copper, silver and gold, used to make coins.

coke: a solid substance left after the gases have been extracted from coal.

colloid: a mixture of ultramicroscopic particles dispersed uniformly through a second substance to form a suspension which may be almost like a solution or may set to a jelly (gel). The word comes from the Greek for glue.

colorimeter: an instrument for measuring the light-absorbing power of a substance. The absorption gives an accurate indication of the concentration of some coloured solutions.

combustion: a reaction in which an element or compound is oxidised to release energy. Some combustion reactions are slow, such as the combustion of the sugar we eat to provide our energy. If the combustion results in a flame, it is called burning. A flame occurs where *gases* combust and release heat and light. At least two gases are therefore required if there is to be a flame. *Example:* the combustion or burning of methane gas (CH_4) in oxygen gas (O_2) produces carbon dioxide (CO_2) and water (H_2O) and gives out heat and light. Some combustion reactions produce light and heat but do not produce flames. *Example:* the combustion of carbon in oxygen produces an intense red–white light but no flame.

combustion spoon: also known as a deflagrating spoon, it consists of a long metal handle with a small cup at the end. Its purpose is to allow the safe introduction of a (usually heated) substance into a gas jar filled with gas, when the reaction is likely to be vigorous. *Example:* the introduction of a heated sodium pellet into a gas jar containing chlorine.

compound: a chemical consisting of two or more elements chemically bonded together. *Example:* Calcium can combine with carbon and oxygen to make calcium carbonate ($CaCO_3$), a compound of all three elements.

condensation: the formation of a liquid from a gas. This is a change of state, also called a phase change.

condensation nuclei: microscopic particles of dust, salt and other materials suspended in the air, that attract water molecules. The usual result is the formation of water droplets.

condensation polymer: a polymer formed by a chain of reactions in which a water molecule is eliminated as every link of the polymer is formed. *Examples:* polyesters, proteins, nylon.

conduction: (i) the exchange of heat (heat conduction) by contact with another object, or (ii) allowing the flow of electrons (electrical conduction).

conductivity: the ability of a substance to conduct. The conductivity of a solution depends on there being suitable free ions in the solution. A conducting solution is called an electrolyte. *Example:* dilute sulphuric acid.

convection: the exchange of heat energy with the surroundings produced by the flow of a fluid due to being heated or cooled.

corrosion: the oxidation of a metal. Corrosion is often regarded as unwanted and is more generally used to refer to the *slow* decay of a metal resulting from contact with gases and liquids in the environment. *Example:* Rust is the corrosion of iron.

corrosive: causing corrosion.

covalent bond: this is the most common form of strong chemical bonding and occurs when two atoms *share* electrons. *Example:* oxygen (O_2)

cracking: breaking down complex molecules into simpler compounds, as in oil refining.

crucible: a small bowl with a lip, made of heat-resistant white glazed ceramic. It is used for heating substances using a Bunsen flame.

crude oil: a chemical mixture of petroleum liquids. Crude oil forms the raw material for an oil refinery.

crystal: a substance that has grown freely so that it can develop external faces. Compare crystalline, where the atoms are not free to form individual crystals and amorphous, where the atoms are arranged irregularly.

crystalline: a solid in which the atoms, ions or molecules are organised into an orderly pattern without distinct crystal faces. *Examples:* copper(II) sulphate, sodium chloride. Compare amorphous.

crystallisation: the process in which a solute comes out of solution slowly and forms crystals. *See:* water of crystallisation.

crystal systems: seven patterns or systems into which all crystals can be grouped: cubic, hexagonal, rhombohedral, tetragonal, orthorhombic, monoclinic and triclinic.

cubic crystal system: groupings of crystals that look like cubes.

current: an electric current is produced by a flow of electrons through a conducting solid or ions through a conducting liquid. The rate of a supply of this charge is measured in amperes (A).

decay (radioactive decay): the way that a radioactive element changes into another element due to loss of mass through radiation. *Example:* uranium 238 decays with the loss of an alpha particle to form thorium 234.

decomposition: the break down of a substance (for example, by heat or with the aid of a catalyst) into simpler components. In such a chemical reaction only one substance is involved. *Example:* hydrogen peroxide ($H_2O_2(aq)$) into oxygen ($O_2(g)$) and water ($H_2O(l)$).

decrepitation: when, as part of the decomposition of a substance, cracking sounds are also produced. *Example:* heating of lead nitrate ($Pb(NO_3)_2$).

dehydration: the removal of water from a substance by heating it, placing it in a dry atmosphere or using a drying (dehydrating) reagent such as concentrated sulphuric acid.

density: the mass per unit volume (e.g. g/cm^3).

desalinisation: the removal of all the salts from sea water, by reverse osmosis or heating the water and collecting the distillate. It is a very energy-intensive process.

desiccant: a substance that absorbs water vapour from the air. *Example:* silica gel.

desiccator: a glass bowl and lid containing a shelf. The apparatus is designed to store materials in dry air. A desiccant is placed below the shelf and the substance to be dried is placed on the shelf. The lid makes a gas-tight joint with the bowl.

destructive distillation: the heating of a material so that it decomposes entirely to release all of its volatile components. Destructive distillation is also known as pyrolysis.

detergent: a chemical based on petroleum that removes dirt.

Devarda's alloy: zinc with a trace of copper, which acts as a catalyst for reactions with the zinc.

diaphragm: a semipermeable membrane – a kind of ultrafine mesh filter – that allows only small ions to pass through. It is used in the electrolysis of brine.

diffusion: the slow mixing of one substance with another until the two substances are evenly mixed. Mixing occurs because of differences in concentration within the mixture. Diffusion works rapidly with gases, very slowly with liquids.

diffusion combustion: the form of combustion that occurs when two gases only begin to mix during ignition. As a result the flame is hollow and yellow in colour. *Example:* a candle flame.

dilute acid: an acid whose concentration has been reduced in a large proportion of water.

disinfectant: a chemical that kills bacteria and other microorganisms.

displacement reaction: a reaction that occurs because metals differ in their reactivity. If a more reactive metal is placed in a solution of a less reactive metal compound, a reaction occurs in which the more reactive metal displaces the metal ions in the solution. *Example:* when zinc metal is introduced into a solution of copper(II) sulphate (which thus contains copper ions), zinc goes into solution as zinc ions, while copper is displaced from the solution and forced to precipitate as metallic copper.

dissociate: to break bonds apart. In the case of acids, it means to break up, forming hydrogen ions. This is an example of ionisation. Strong acids dissociate completely. Weak acids are not completely ionised, and a solution of a weak acid has a relatively low concentration of hydrogen ions.

dissolve: to break down a substance in a solution without causing a reaction.

distillation: the process of separating mixtures by condensing the vapours through cooling.

distilled water: distilled water is nearly pure water and is produced by distillation of tap water. Distilled water is used in the laboratory in preference to tap water because the distillation process removes many of the impurities in tap water that may influence the chemical reactions for which the water is used.

Dreschel bottle: a tall bottle with a special stopper, designed to allow a gas to pass through a liquid. The stopper contains both inlet and outlet tubes. One tube extends below the surface of the liquid so that the gas has to pass through the liquid before it can escape to the outlet tube.

dropper funnel: a special funnel with a tap to allow the controlled release of a liquid. Also known as a dropping funnel or tap funnel.

drying agent: *See:* dehydrating agent.

dye: a coloured substance that will stick to another substance so that both appear coloured.

effervesce: to give off bubbles of gas.

effloresce: to lose water and turn to a fine powder on exposure to the air. *Example:* Sodium carbonate on the rim of a reagent bottle stopper.

electrical conductivity: *See:* conductivity

electrical potential: the energy produced by an electrochemical cell and measured by the voltage or electromotive force (emf). *See:* potential difference, electromotive force.

electrochemical cell: a cell consisting of two electrodes and an electrolyte. It can be set up to generate an electric current (usually known as a galvanic cell, an example of which is a battery), or an electric current can be passed through it to produce a chemical reaction (in which case it is called an electrolytic cell and can be used to refine metals or for electroplating).

electrochemical series: the arrangement of substances that are either oxidising or reducing agents in order of strength as a reagent, for example, with the strong oxidising agents at the top of the list and the strong reducing agents at the bottom.

electrode: a conductor that forms one terminal of a cell.

electrolysis: an electrical–chemical process that uses an electric current to cause the break-up of a compound and the movement of metal ions in a solution. The process happens in many natural situations (as for example in rusting) and is also commonly used

in industry for purifying (refining) metals or for plating metal objects with a fine, even metal coating.

electrolyte: an ionic solution that conducts electricity.

electrolytic cell: *See:* electrochemical cell.

electromotive force (emf): the force set up in an electric circuit by a potential difference.

electron: a tiny, negatively charged particle that is part of an atom. The flow of electrons through a solid material such as a wire produces an electric current.

electron configuration: the pattern in which electrons are arranged in shells around the nucleus of an atom. *Example:* chlorine has the configuration 2, 8, 7.

electroplating: depositing a thin layer of a metal on to the surface of another substance using electrolysis.

element: a substance that cannot be decomposed into simpler substance by chemical means. *Examples:* calcium, iron, gold.

emulsion: tiny droplets of one substance dispersed in another. One common oil in water emulsion is called milk. Because the tiny droplets tend to come together, another stabilising substance is often needed. Soaps and detergents are such agents, wrapping the particles of grease and oil in a stable coat. Photographic film is an example of a solid emulsion.

endothermic reaction: a reaction that takes in heat. *Example:* when ammonium chloride is dissolved in water.

end point: the stage in a titration when the reaction between the titrant (added from a burette) and the titrate (in the flask) is complete. The end point is normally recognised by use of an indicator which has been added to

the titrate. In an acid–base reaction this is also called the neutralisation point.

enzyme: biological catalysts in the form of proteins in the body that speed up chemical reactions. Every living cell contains hundreds of enzymes that help the processes of life continue.

ester: organic compounds formed by the reaction of an alcohol with an acid and which often have a fruity taste. *Example:* ethyl acetate ($CH_3COOC_2H_5$).

evaporation: the change of state of a liquid to a gas. Evaporation happens below the boiling point and is used as a method of separating the materials in a solution.

excess, to: if a reactant has been added to another reactant in excess, it has exceeded the amount required to complete the reaction.

exothermic reaction: a reaction that gives out substantial amounts of heat. *Example:* sucrose and concentrated sulphuric acid.

explosive: a substance which, when a shock is applied to it, decomposes very rapidly, releasing a very large amount of heat and creating a large volume of gases as a shock wave.

fats: semisolid, energy-rich compounds derived from plants or animals, made of carbon, hydrogen and oxygen. These are examples of esters.

ferment: to break down a substance by microorganisms in the absence of oxygen. *Example:* fermentation of sugar to ethanol during the production of alcoholic drinks.

filtrate: the liquid that has passed through a filter.

filtration: the separation of a liquid from a solid using a membrane with small holes (i.e. a filter paper).

flame: a mixture of gases undergoing burning. A solid or liquid must produce a gas before it can react with oxygen and burn with a flame.

flammable (also inflammable): able to burn (in air). *Opposite:* non-flammable.

flocculation: the grouping together of small particles in a suspension to form particles large enough to settle out as a precipitate. Flocculation is usually caused by the presence of a flocculating agent. *Example:* calcium ions are the flocculating agent for suspended clay particles.

fluid: able to flow; either a liquid or a gas.

fluorescent: a substance that gives out visible light when struck by invisible waves, such as ultraviolet rays.

flux: a material used to make it easier for a liquid to flow. A flux dissolves metal oxides and so prevents a metal from oxidising while being heated.

foam: a substance that is sufficiently gelatinous to be able to contain bubbles of gas. The gas bulks up the substance, making it behave as though it were semirigid.

fossil fuels: hydrocarbon compounds that have been formed from buried plant and animal remains. High pressures and temperatures lasting over millions of years are required. *Examples:* The fossil fuels are coal, oil and natural gas.

fraction: a group of similar components of a mixture. *Example:* In the petroleum industry the light fractions of crude oil are those with the smallest molecules, while the medium and heavy fractions have larger molecules.

fractional distillation: the separation of the components of a liquid mixture by heating them to their boiling points.

fractionating column: a glass column designed to allow different fractions to be separated when they boil. In industry, it may be called a fractionating tower.

free radical: a very reactive atom or group with a 'spare' electron. *Example:* methyl, $CH_3\bullet$.

freezing point: the temperature at which a substance undergoes a phase change from a liquid to a solid. It is the same temperature as the melting point.

fuel: a concentrated form of chemical energy. The main sources of fuels (called fossil fuels because they were formed by geological processes) are coal, crude oil and natural gas.

fuel rods: the rods of uranium or other radioactive material used as a fuel in nuclear power stations.

fume chamber or fume cupboard: a special laboratory chamber fitted with a protective glass shield and containing a powerful extraction fan to remove toxic fumes.

fuming: an unstable liquid that gives off a gas. Very concentrated acid solutions are often fuming solutions. *Example:* fuming nitric acid.

galvanising: applying a thin zinc coating to protect another metal.

gamma rays: waves of radiation produced as the nucleus of a radioactive element rearranges itself into a tighter cluster of protons and neutrons. Gamma rays carry enough energy to damage living cells.

gangue: the unwanted material in an ore.

gas/gaseous phase: a form of matter in which the molecules form no definite shape and are free to move about to uniformly fill any vessel they are put in. A gas can easily be compressed into a much smaller volume.

gas syringe: a glass syringe with a graduated cylinder designed to collect and measure small amounts of gases produced during an experiment.

gelatinous precipitate: a precipitate that has a jelly-like appearance. *Example:* iron(III) hydroxide. Because a gelatinous precipitate is mostly water, it is of a similar density to water and will float or lie suspended in the liquid. *See:* granular precipitate.

glass: a transparent silicate without any crystal growth. It has a glassy lustre and breaks with a curved fracture. Note that some minerals have all these features and are therefore natural glasses. Household glass is a synthetic silicate.

glucose: the most common of the natural sugars ($C_6H_{12}O_6$). It occurs as the polymer known as cellulose, the fibre in plants. Starch is also a form of glucose.

granular precipitate: a precipitate that has a grain-like appearance. *Example:* lead(II) hydroxide. *See:* gelatinous precipitate.

gravimetric analysis: a quantitative form of analysis in which the mass (weight) of the reactants and products is measured.

group: a vertical column in the Periodic Table. There are eight groups in the table. Their numbers correspond to the number of electrons in the outer shell of the atoms in the group. *Example:* Group 2 contains beryllium, magnesium, calcium, strontium, barium and radium.

Greenhouse Effect: an increase in the global air temperature as a result of heat released from burning fossil fuels being absorbed by carbon dioxide in the atmosphere.

Greenhouse gas: any of the various gases that contribute to the Greenhouse Effect. *Example:* carbon dioxide.

half-life: the time it takes for the radiation coming from a sample of a radioactive element to decrease by half.

halide: a salt of one of the halogens.

halogen: one of a group of elements including chlorine, bromine, iodine and fluorine in Group 7 of the Periodic Table.

heat: the energy that is transferred when a substance is at a different temperature to that of its surroundings. *See:* endothermic and exothermic reactions.

heat capacity: the ratio of the heat supplied to a substance, compared with the rise in temperature that is produced.

heat of combustion: the amount of heat given off by a mole of a substance during combustion. This heat is a property of the substance and is the same no matter what kind of combustion is involved. *Example:* heat of combustion of carbon is 94.05 kcal (✗ 4.18 = 393.1 kJ).

hydrate: a solid compound in crystalline form that contains water molecules. Hydrates commonly form when a solution of a soluble salt is evaporated. The water that forms part of a hydrate crystal is known as the 'water of crystallisation'. It can usually be removed by heating, leaving an anhydrous salt.

hydration: the process of absorption of water by a substance. In some cases hydration makes the substance change colour; in many other cases there is no colour change, simply a change in volume. *Example:* dark blue hydrated copper(II) sulphate ($CuSO_4 \bullet 5H_2O$) can be heated to produce white anhydrous copper(II) sulphate ($CuSO_4$).

hydride: a compound containing just hydrogen and another element, most often a metal.

Examples: water (H_2O), methane (CH_4) and phosphine (PH_3).

hydrous: hydrated with water. *See:* anhydrous.

hydrocarbon: a compound in which only hydrogen and carbon atoms are present. Most fuels are hydrocarbons, as is the simple plastic, polyethene. *Example:* methane CH_4.

hydrogen bond: a type of attractive force that holds one molecule to another. It is one of the weaker forms of intermolecular attractive force. *Example:* hydrogen bonds occur in water.

ignition temperature: the temperature at which a substance begins to burn.

immiscible: will not mix with another substance. e.g. oil and water.

incandescent: glowing or shining with heat. *Example:* tungsten filament in an incandescent light bulb.

incomplete combustion: combustion in which only some of the reactant or reactants combust, or the products are not those that would be obtained if all the reactions went to completion. It is uncommon for combustion to be complete and incomplete combustion is more frequent. *Example:* incomplete combustion of carbon in oxygen produces carbon monoxide and not carbon dioxide.

indicator (acid–base indicator): a substance or mixture of substances used to test the acidity or alkalinity of a substance. An indicator changes colour depending on the acidity of the solution being tested. Many indicators are complicated organic substances. Some indicators used in the laboratory include Universal Indicator, litmus, phenolphthalein, methyl orange and bromothymol. *See:* Universal Indicator.

induction period: the time taken for a reaction to reach ignition temperature. During this period, no apparent reaction occurs, then the materials appear to undergo spontaneous combustion.

inert: unreactive.

inhibitor: a substance that prevents a reaction from occurring.

inorganic substance: a substance that does not contain carbon and hydrogen. *Examples:* NaCl, $CaCO_3$.

insoluble: a substance that will not dissolve.

ion: an atom, or group of atoms, that has gained or lost one or more electrons and so developed an electrical charge. Ions behave differently from electrically neutral atoms and molecules. They can move in an electric field, and they can also bind strongly to solvent molecules such as water. Positively charged ions are called cations; negatively charged ions are called anions. Ions can carry an electrical current through solutions.

ionic bond: the form of bonding that occurs between two ions when the ions have opposite charges. *Example:* sodium cations bond with chloride anions to form common salt (NaCl) when a salty solution is evaporated. Ionic bonds are strong bonds except in the presence of a solvent. *See:* bond.

ionic compound: a compound that consists of ions. *Example:* NaCl.

ionisation: a process that creates ions.

ionise: to break up neutral molecules into oppositely charged ions or to convert atoms into ions by the loss of electrons.

isotope: one of two or more atoms of the same element that have the same number of protons in their nucleus (atomic number), but which have a different number of neutrons (atomic mass). *Example:* carbon-12 and carbon-14.

Kipp's apparatus: a special piece of glassware consisting of three chambers, designed to provide a continuous and regulated production of gas by bringing the reactants into contact in a controlled way.

lanthanide series or lanthanide metals: a series of 15 similar metallic elements between lanthanum and lutetium. They are transition metals and also also called rare earths.

latent heat: the amount of heat that is absorbed or released during the process of changing state between gas, liquid or solid. For example, heat is absorbed when a substance melts and it is released again when the substance solidifies.

lattice: a regular arrangement of atoms, ions or molecules in a crystalline solid.

leaching: the extraction of a substance by percolating a solvent through a material. *Example:* when water flows through an ore, some of the heavy metals in it may be leached out causing environmental pollution.

Liebig condenser: a piece of glassware consisting of a sloping water-cooled tube. The design allows a volatile material to be condensed and collected.

liquefaction: to make something liquid.

liquid/liquid phase: a form of matter that has a fixed volume but no fixed shape.

lime (quicklime): calcium oxide (CaO). A white, caustic solid, manufactured by heating limestone and used for making mortar, fertiliser or bleach.

limewater: an aqueous solution of calcium hydroxide, used especially to detect the presence of carbon dioxide.

litmus: an indicator obtained from lichens. Used as a solution or impregnated into paper (litmus paper), which is dampened before use. Litmus turns red under acid conditions and purple in alkaline conditions. Litmus is a crude indicator when compared with Universal Indicator.

load (electronics): an impedance or circuit that receives or develops the output of a cell or other power supply.

lustre: the shininess of a substance.

malleable: able to be pressed or hammered into shape.

manometer: a device for measuring gas pressure. A simple manometer is made by partly filling a U-shaped rubber tube with water and connecting one end to the source of gas whose pressure is to be measured. The pressure is always relative to atmospheric pressure.

mass: the amount of matter in an object. In everyday use the word weight is often used (somewhat incorrectly) to mean mass.

matter: anything that has mass and takes up space.

melting point: the temperature at which a substance changes state from a solid phase to a liquid phase. It is the same as freezing point.

membrane: a thin, flexible sheet. A semipermeable membrane has microscopic holes of a size that will selectively allow some ions and molecules to pass through but hold others back. It thus acts as a kind of filter. *Example:* a membrane used for osmosis.

meniscus: the curved surface of a liquid that forms in a small bore or capillary tube. The meniscus is convex (bulges upwards) for mercury and is concave (sags downwards) for water.

metal: a class of elements that is a good conductor of electricity and heat, has a metallic lustre, is malleable and ductile, forms

cations and has oxides that are bases. Metals are formed as cations held together by a sea of electrons. A metal may also be an alloy of these elements. *Example:* sodium, calcium, gold. *See:* alloy, metalloid, non-metal.

metallic bonding: cations reside in a 'sea' of mobile electrons. It allows metals to be good conductors and means that they are not brittle. *See:* bonding.

metallic lustre: *See:* lustre.

metalloid: a class of elements intermediate in properties between metals and non-metals. Metalloids are also called semi-metals or semiconductors. *Example:* silicon, germanium, antimony. *See:* metal, non-metal, semiconductor.

micronutrient: an element that the body requires in small amounts. Another term is trace element.

mineral: a solid substance made of just one element or compound. *Example:* calcite is a mineral because it consists only of calcium carbonate; halite is a mineral because it contains only sodium chloride.

mineral acid: an acid that does not contain carbon and which attacks minerals. Hydrochloric, sulphuric and nitric acids are the main mineral acids.

miscible: capable of being mixed.

mixing combustion: the form of combustion that occurs when two gases thoroughly mix before they ignite and so produce almost complete combustion. *Example:* when a Bunsen flame is blue.

mixture: a material that can be separated into two or more substances using physical means. *Example:* a mixture of copper(II) sulphate and cadmium sulphide can be separated by filtration.

molar mass: the mass per mole of atoms of an element. It has the same value and uses the same units

as atomic weight. *Example:* molar mass of chlorine is 35.45 g/mol. *See:* atomic weight.

mole: 1 mole is the amount of a substance which contains Avagadro's number (6×10^{23}) of particles. *Example:* 1 mole of carbon-12 weighs exactly 12 g.

molecular mass: *See:* molar mass.

molecular weight: *See:* molar mass.

molecule: a group of two or more atoms held together by chemical bonds. *Example:* O_2.

monoclinic system: a grouping of crystals that look like double-ended chisel blades.

monomer: a small molecule and building block for larger chain molecules or polymers ('mono' means one, 'mer' means part). *Examples:* tetrafluoroethene for teflon, ethene for polyethene.

native element: an element that occurs in an uncombined state. *Examples:* sulphur, gold.

native metal: a pure form of a metal, not combined as a compound. Native metal is more common in poorly reactive elements than in those that are very reactive. *Examples:* copper, gold.

net ionic reaction: the overall, or net, change that occurs in a reaction, seen in terms of ions.

neutralisation: the reaction of acids and bases to produce a salt and water. The reaction causes hydrogen from the acid and hydroxide from the base to be changed to water. *Example:* hydrochloric acid reacts with, and neutralises, sodium hydroxide to form the salt sodium chloride (common salt) and water. The term is more generally used for any reaction in which the pH changes toward 7.0, which is the pH of a neutral solution. *See:* pH.

neutralisation point: *See:* end point.

neutron: a particle inside the nucleus of an atom that is neutral and has no charge.

newton (N): the unit of force required to give one kilogram an acceleration of one metre per second every second (1 ms^{-2}).

nitrate: a compound that includes nitrogen and oxygen and contains more oxygen than a nitrite. Nitrate ions have the chemical formula NO_3^-. *Examples:* sodium nitrate $NaNO_3$ and lead nitrate $Pb(NO_3)_2$.

nitrite: a compound that includes nitrogen and oxygen and contains less oxygen than a nitrate. Nitrite ions have the chemical formula NO_2^-. *Example:* sodium nitrite $NaNO_2$.

noble gases: the members of Group 8 of the Periodic Table: helium, neon, argon, krypton, xenon, radon. These gases are almost entirely unreactive.

noble metals: silver, gold, platinum and mercury. These are the least reactive metals.

non-combustible: a substance that will not combust or burn. *Example:* carbon dioxide.

non-metal: a brittle substance that does not conduct electricity. *Examples:* sulphur, phosphorus, all gases. *See:* metal, metalloid.

normal salt: salts that do not contain a hydroxide (OH^-) ion, which would make them basic salts, or a hydrogen ion, which would make them acid salts. *Example:* sodium chloride (NaCl).

nucleus: the small, positively charged particle at the centre of an atom. The nucleus is responsible for most of the mass of an atom.

opaque: a substance that will not transmit light so that it is impossible to see through it. Most solids are opaque.

ore: a rock containing enough of a useful substance to make mining it

worthwhile. *Example:* bauxite, aluminium ore.

organic acid: an acid containing carbon and hydrogen. *Example:* methanoic (formic) acid (HCOOH).

organic chemistry: the study of organic compounds.

organic compound (organic substance; organic material): a compound (or substance) that contains carbon and usually hydrogen. (The carbonates are usually excluded.) *Examples:* methane (CH_4), chloromethane (CH_3Cl), ethene (C_2H_4), ethanol (C_2H_5OH), ethanoic acid (C_2H_3OOH), etc.

organic solvent: an organic substance that will dissolve other substances. *Example:* carbon tetrachloride (CCl_4).

osmosis: a process whereby molecules of a liquid solvent move through a semipermeable membrane from a region of low concentration of a solute to a region with a high concentration of a solute.

oxidation: combination with oxygen or a reaction in which an atom, ion or molecule loses electrons to an oxidising agent. (Note that an oxidising agent does not have to contain oxygen.) The opposite of oxidation is reduction. *See:* reduction.

oxidation number (oxidation state): the effective charge on an atom in a compound. An increase in oxidation number corresponds to oxidation, and a decrease to reduction. Shown in Roman numerals. *Example:* manganate(IV).

oxidation–reduction reaction (redox reaction): reaction in which oxidation and reduction occurs; a reaction in which electrons are transferred. *Example:* copper and oxygen react to produce copper(II) oxide. The copper is oxidised, and oxygen is reduced.

oxidation state: *See:* oxidation number.

oxide: a compound that includes oxygen and one other element. *Example:* copper oxide (CuO).

oxidise: to combine with or gain oxygen or to react such that an atom, ion or molecule loses electrons to an oxidising agent.

oxidising agent: a substance that removes electrons from another substance being oxidised (and therefore is itself reduced) in a redox reaction. *Example:* chlorine (Cl_2).

ozone: a form of oxygen whose molecules contain three atoms of oxygen. Ozone is regarded as a beneficial gas when high in the atmosphere because it blocks ultraviolet rays. It is a harmful gas when breathed in, so low level ozone which is produced as part of city smog is regarded as a form of pollution. The ozone layer is the uppermost part of the stratosphere.

partial pressure: the pressure a gas in a mixture would exert if it alone occupied a flask. *Example:* oxygen makes up about a fifth of the atmosphere. Its partial pressure is therefore about a fifth of normal atmospheric pressure.

pascal: the unit of pressure, equal to one newton per square metre of surface. *See:* newton.

patina: a surface coating that develops on metals and protects them from further corrosion. *Example:* the green coating of copper carbonate that forms on copper statues.

percolate: to move slowly through the pores of a rock.

period: a row in the Periodic Table.

Periodic Table: a chart organising elements by atomic number and chemical properties into groups and periods.

pestle and mortar: a pestle is a ceramic rod with a rounded end, a mortar is a ceramic dish. Pestle and mortar are used together to pound or grind solids into fine powders.

Petri dish: a shallow glass or plastic dish with a lid.

petroleum: a natural mixture of a range of gases, liquids and solids derived from the decomposed remains of plants and animals.

pH: a measure of the hydrogen ion concentration in a liquid. Neutral is pH 7.0; numbers greater than this are alkaline; smaller numbers are acidic. *See:* neutralisation, acid, base.

pH meter: a device that accurately measures the pH of a solution. A pH meter is a voltmeter that measures the electric potential difference between two electrodes (which are attached to the meter through a probe) when they are submerged in a solution. The readings are shown on a dial or digital display.

phase: a particular state of matter. A substance may exist as a solid, liquid or gas and may change between these phases with addition or removal of energy. *Examples:* ice, liquid and vapour are the three phases of water. Ice undergoes a phase change to water when heat energy is added.

phosphor: any material that glows when energised by ultraviolet or electron beams, such as in fluorescent tubes and cathode ray tubes. Phosphors, such as phosphorus, emit light after the source of excitation is cut off. This is why they glow in the dark. By contrast, fluorescers, such as fluorite, only emit light while they are being excited by ultraviolet light or an electron beam.

photochemical smog: photochemical reactions are caused by the energy of sunlight. Photochemical smog is a mixture of tiny particles and a brown haze caused by the reaction of colourless nitric oxide from vehicle exhausts and oxygen of the air to form brown nitrogen dioxide.

photon: a parcel of light energy.

photosynthesis: the process by which plants use the energy of the Sun to make the compounds they need for life. In photosynthesis, six molecules of carbon dioxide from the air combine with six molecules of water, forming one molecule of glucose (sugar) and releasing six molecules of oxygen back into the atmosphere.

pipe-clay triangle: a device made from three small pieces of ceramic tube which are wired together in the shape of a triangle. Pipe-clay triangles are used to support round-bottomed dishes when they are heated in a Bunsen flame.

pipette: a log, slender, glass tube used, in conjunction with a pipette filler, to draw up and then transfer accurately measured amounts of liquid.

plastic: (material) a carbon-based substance consisting of long chains (polymers) of simple molecules. The word plastic is commonly restricted to synthetic polymers. *Examples:* polyvinyl chloride, nylon: **(property)** a material is plastic if it can be made to change shape easily. Plastic materials will remain in the new shape. (Compare with elastic, a property whereby a material goes back to its original shape.)

pneumatic trough: a shallow water-filled glass dish used to house a beehive shelf and a gas jar as part of the apparatus for collecting a gas over water.

polar solvent: a solvent in which the atoms have partial electric charges. *Example:* water.

polymer: a compound that is made of long chains by combining molecules (called monomers) as repeating units. ('Poly' means many, 'mer' means part.) *Examples:* polytetrafluoroethene or Teflon from tetrafluoroethene, Terylene from terephthalic acid and ethane-1,2-diol (ethylene glycol).

polymerisation: a chemical reaction in which large numbers of similar molecules arrange themselves into large molecules, usually long chains. This process usually happens when there is a suitable catalyst present. *Example:* ethene gas reacts to form polyethene in the presence of certain catalysts.

polymorphism: (meaning many shapes) the tendency of some materials to have more than one solid form. *Example:* carbon as diamond, graphite and buckminsterfullerene.

porous: a material containing many small holes or cracks. Quite often the pores are connected, and liquids, such as water or oil, can move through them.

potential difference: a measure of the work that must be done to move an electric charge from one point to the other in a circuit. Potential difference is measured in volts (V). *See:* electrical potential.

precious metal: silver, gold, platinum, iridium and palladium. Each is prized for its rarity.

precipitate: a solid substance formed as a result of a chemical reaction between two liquids or gases. *Example:* iron(III) hydroxide is precipitated when sodium hydroxide solution is added to iron(III) chloride. *See:* gelatinous precipitate, granular precipitate.

preservative: a substance that prevents the natural organic decay processes from occurring. Many substances can be used safely for this purpose, including sulphites and nitrogen gas.

pressure: the force per unit area measured in pascals. *See:* pascal, atmospheric pressure.

product: a substance produced by a chemical reaction. *Example:* when the reactants copper and oxygen react, they produce the product, copper oxide.

proton: a positively charged particle in the nucleus of an atom that balances out the charge of the surrounding electrons.

proton number: this is the modern expression for atomic number. *See:* atomic number.

purify: to remove all impurities from a mixture, perhaps by precipitation, or filtration.

pyrolysis: chemical decomposition brought about by heat. *Example:* decomposition of lead nitrate. *See:* destructive distillation.

pyrometallurgy: refining a metal from its ore using heat. A blast furnace or smelter is the main equipment used.

quantitative: measurement of the amounts of constituents of a substance, for example by mass or volume. *See:* gravimetric analysis, volumetric analysis.

radiation: the exchange of energy with the surroundings through the transmission of waves or particles of energy. Radiation is a form of energy transfer that can happen through space; no intervening medium is required (as would be the case for conduction and convection).

radical: an atom, molecule, or ion with at least one unpaired electron. *Example:* nitrogen monoxide (NO).

radioactive: emitting radiation or particles from the nucleus of its atoms.

radioactive decay: a change in a radioactive element due to loss of mass through radiation. For example, uranium decays (changes) to lead.

reactant: a starting material that takes part in, and undergoes, change during a chemical reaction. *Example:* hydrochloric acid and calcium carbonate are reactants; the reaction produces the products calcium chloride, carbon dioxide and water.

reaction: the recombination of two substances using parts of each substance to produce new substances. *Example:* the reactants sodium chloride and sulphuric acid react and recombine to form the products sodium sulphate, chlorine and water.

reactivity: the tendency of a substance to react with other substances. The term is most widely used in comparing the reactivity of metals. Metals are arranged in a reactivity series.

reactivity series: the series of metals organised in order of their reactivity, with the most reactive metals, such as sodium, at the top and the least react metals, such as gold, at the bottom. Hydrogen is usually included in the series for comparative purposes.

reagent: a commonly available substance (reactant) used to create a reaction. Reagents are the chemicals normally kept on chemistry laboratory benches. Many substances called reagents are most commonly used for test purposes.

redox reaction (oxidation–reduction reaction): a reaction that involves oxidation and reduction; a reactions in which electrons are transferred. *See:* oxidation–reduction.

reducing agent: a substance that gives electrons to another substance being reduced (and therefore itself being oxidised) in a redox reaction. *Example:* hydrogen sulphide (H_2S).

reduction: the removal of oxygen from, or the addition of hydrogen to, a compound. Also a reaction in which an atom, ion or molecule gains electrons from an reducing agent. (The opposite of reduction is oxidation.)

reduction tube: a boiling tube with a small hole near the closed end. The tube is mounted horizontally, a sample is placed in the tube and a reducing gas, such as carbon monoxide, is passed through the tube. The oxidised gas escapes through the small hole.

refining: separating a mixture into the simpler substances of which it is made.

reflux distillation system: a form of distillation using a Liebig condenser placed vertically, so that all the vapours created during boiling are condensed back into the liquid, rather than escaping. In this way, the concentration of all the reactants remains constant.

relative atomic mass: in the past a measure of the mass of an atom on a scale relative to the mass of an atom of hydrogen, where hydrogen is 1. Nowadays a measure of the mass of an atom relative to the mass of one twelfth of an atom of carbon-12. If the relative atomic mass is given as a rounded figure, it is called an approximate relative atomic mass. *Examples:* chlorine 35, calcium 40, gold 197. *See:* atomic mass, atomic weight.

reversible reaction: a reaction in which the products can be transformed back into their original chemical form. *Example:* heated iron reacts with steam to produce iron oxide and hydrogen. If the hydrogen is passed over this heated oxide, it forms iron and steam. $3Fe + 4H_2O \rightleftharpoons Fe_3O_4 + 4H_2$.

roast: heating a substance for a long time at a high temperature, as in a furnace.

rust: the product of the corrosion of iron and steel in the presence of air and water.

salt: a compound, often involving a metal, that is the reaction product of an acid and a base, or of two elements. (Note 'salt' is also the common word for sodium chloride, common salt or table salt.) *Example:* sodium chloride (NaCl) and potassium sulphate (K_2SO_4) *See:* acid salt, basic salt, normal salt.

salt bridge: a permeable material soaked in a salt solution that allows ions to be transferred from one container to another. The salt solution remains unchanged during this transfer. *Example:* sodium sulphate used as a salt bridge in a galvanic cell.

saponification: a reaction between a fat and a base that produces a soap.

saturated: a state in which a liquid can hold no more of a substance. If any more of the substance is added, it will not dissolve.

saturated hydrocarbon: a hydrocarbon in which the carbon atoms are held with single bonds. *Example:* ethane (C_2H_6).

saturated solution: a solution that holds the maximum possible amount of dissolved material. When saturated, the rate of dissolving solid and that of recrystallisation solid are the same, and a condition of equilibrium is reached. The amount of material in solution varies with the temperature; cold solutions can hold less dissolved solid material than hot solutions. Gases are more soluble in cold liquids than in hot liquids.

sediment: material that settles out at the bottom of a liquid when it is still. A precipitate is one form of sediment.

semiconductor: a material of intermediate conductivity. Semiconductor devices often use

silicon when they are made as part of diodes, transistors or integrated circuits. Elements intermediate between metals and non-metals are also sometimes called semiconductors. *Example:* germanium oxide, germanium. *See:* metalloid.

semipermeable membrane: a thin material that acts as a fine sieve or filter, allowing small molecules to pass, but holding large molecules back.

separating column: used in chromatography. A tall glass tube containing a porous disc near the base and filled with a substance (for example, aluminium oxide, which is known as a stationary phase) that can adsorb materials on its surface. When a mixture is passed through the column, fractions are retarded by differing amounts, so that each fraction is washed through the column in sequence.

separating funnel: a pear-shaped, glassware funnel designed to permit the separation of immiscible liquids by simply pouring off the more dense liquid while leaving the less dense liquid in the funnel.

series circuit: an electrical circuit in which all of the components are joined end to end in a line.

shell: the term used to describe the imaginary ball-shaped surface outside the nucleus of an atom that would be formed by a set of electrons of similar energy. The outermost shell is known as the valence shell. *Example:* neon has shells containing 2 and 8 electrons.

side-arm boiling tube: a boiling tube with an integral glass pipe near its open end. The side arm is normally used for the entry or exit of a gas.

simple distillation: the distillation of a substance when only one volatile fraction is to be collected. Simple distillation uses a Liebig

condenser arranged almost horizontally. When the liquid mixture is heated and vapours are produced, they enter the condenser and then flow away from the flask and can be collected. *Example:* simple distillation of ethanoic acid.

slag: a mixture of substances that are waste products of a furnace. Most slags are composed mainly of silicates.

smelting: roasting a substance in order to extract the metal contained in it.

smog: a mixture of smoke and fog. The term is used to describe city fogs in which there is a large proportion of particulate matter (tiny pieces of carbon from exhausts) and also a high concentration of sulphur and nitrogen gases and probably ozone. *See:* photochemical smog.

smokeless fuel: a fuel which has been subjected to partial pyrolysis, such that there is no more loose particulate matter remaining. *Example:* Coke is a smokeless fuel.

solid/solid phase: a rigid form of matter which maintains its shape, whatever its container.

solubility: a measure of the maximum amount of a substance that can be contained in a solvent.

soluble: readily dissolvable in a solvent.

solute: a substance that has dissolved. *Example:* sodium chloride in water.

solution: a mixture of a liquid (the solvent) and at least one other substance of lesser abundance (the solute). Mixtures can be separated by physical means, for example, by evaporation and cooling. *See:* aqueous solution.

solvent: the main substance in a solution.

spectator ions: the ionic part of a compound that does not play an active part in a reaction. *Example:* when magnesium ribbon is placed in copper(II) sulphate solution, the copper is displaced from the solution by the magnesium, while the sulphate ion (SO_4^{2-}) plays no part in the reaction and so behaves as a spectator ion.

spectrum: a progressive series arranged using a characteristic etc. *Examples:* the range of colours that make up visible light (as seen in a rainbow) or across all electromagnetic radiation, arranged in progression according to their wavelength.

spontaneous combustion: the effect of a very reactive material or combination of reactants that suddenly reach their ignition temperature and begin to combust rapidly.

standard temperature and pressure (STP): 0°C at one atmosphere (a pressure which supports a column of mercury 760 mm high). Also given as 0°C at 100 kilopascals. *See:* atmospheric pressure.

state of matter: the physical form of matter. There are three states of matter: liquid, solid and gaseous.

stationary phase: a name given to a material which is used as a medium for separating a liquid mixture in chromatography.

strong acid: an acid that has completely dissociated (ionised) in water. Mineral acids are strong acids.

sublime/sublimation: the change of a substance from solid to gas, or vice versa, without going through a liquid phase. *Example:* iodine sublimes from a purple solid to a purple gas.

substance: a type of material, including mixtures.

sulphate: a compound that includes sulphur and oxygen and contains more oxygen than a sulphite. Sulphate ions have the chemical formula SO_4^{2-}. *Examples:* calcium sulphate $CaSO_4$ (the main constituent of gypsum) and aluminium sulphate $Al_2(SO_4)_3$ (an alum).

sulphide: a sulphur compound that contains no oxygen. Sulphide ions have the chemical formula S^{2-}. *Example:* hydrogen sulphide (H_2S).

sulphite: a compound that includes sulphur and oxygen but contains less oxygen than a sulphate. Sulphite ions have the chemical formula SO_3^{2-}. *Example:* sodium sulphite Na_2SO_3.

supercooling: the ability of some substances to cool below their normal freezing point. *Example:* sodium thiosulphate.

supersaturated solution: a solution in which the amount of solute is greater than that which would normally be expected in a saturated solution. Most solids are more soluble in hot solutions than in cold. If a hot saturated solution is made up, the solution can be rapidly cooled down below its freezing point before it begins to solidify. This is a supersaturated solution.

surface tension: the force that operates on the surface of a liquid and which makes it act as though it were covered with an invisible, elastic film.

suspension: a mist of tiny particles in a liquid.

synthesis: a reaction in which a substance is formed from simpler reactants. *Example:* hydrogen gas and chlorine gas react to sythesise hydrogen chloride gas. The term can also be applied to polymerisation of organic compounds.

synthetic: does not occur naturally but has to be manufactured. Commonly used in the name 'synthetic fibre'.

tare: an allowance made for the weight of a container.

tarnish: a coating that develops as a result of the reaction between a metal and substances in the air. The most common form of tarnishing is a very thin, transparent oxide coating.

terminal: one of the electrodes of a battery.

test (chemical): a reagent or a procedure used to reveal the presence of another reagent. *Example:* litmus and other indicators are used to test the acidity or alkalinity of a substance.

test tube: A thin, glass tube, closed at one end and used for chemical tests, etc. The composition and thickness of the glass is such that, while it is inert to most chemical reactions, it may not sustain very high temperatures but can usually be heated in a Bunsen flame. *See:* boiling tube.

thermal decomposition: the breakdown of a substance using heat. *See:* pyrolysis.

thermoplastic: a plastic that will soften and can be moulded repeatedly into shape on heating and will set into the moulded shape as it cools.

thermoset: a plastic that will set into a moulded shape as it cools, but which cannot be made soft by reheating.

thistle funnel: a narrow tube, expanded at the top into a thistlehead-shaped vessel. It is used as a funnel when introducing small amounts of liquid reactant. When fitted with a tap, it can be used to control the rate of entry of a reactant. *See:* burette.

titration: the analysis of the composition of a substance in a solution by measuring the volume of that solution (the titrant, normally in a burette) needed to react with a given volume of another solution (the titrate, normally placed in a flask). An indicator is often used to signal change. *Example:* neutralisation of sodium hydroxide using hydrochloric acid in an acid–base titration. *See:* end point.

toxic: poisonous.

transition metals: the group of metals that belong to the d-block of the Periodic Table. Transition metals commonly have a number of differently coloured oxidation states. *Examples:* iron, vanadium.

Universal Indicator: a mixture of indicators commonly used in the laboratory because of its reliability. Used as a solution or impregnated into paper (Indicator paper), which is dampened before use. Universal Indicator changes colour from purple in a strongly alkaline solution through green when the solution is neutral to red in strongly acidic solutions. Universal Indicator is more accurate than litmus paper but less accurate than a pH meter.

unsaturated hydrocarbon: a hydrocarbon, in which at least one bond is a double or triple bond. Hydrogen atoms can be added to unsaturated compounds to form saturated compounds. *Example:* ethene, C_2H_4 or $CH_2{=}CH_2$.

vacuum: a container from which air has been removed using a pump.

valency: the number of bonds that an atom can form. *Examples:* calcium has a valency of 2 and bromine a valency of 1

valency shell: the outermost shell of an atom. *See:* shell.

vapour: the gaseous phase of a substance that is a liquid or a solid at that temperature. *Examples:* water vapour is the gaseous form of water, iodine vapour is the gaseous form of solid iodine. *See:* gas.

vein: a fissure in rock that has filled with ore or other mineral-bearing rock.

viscous: slow-moving, syrupy. A liquid that has a low viscosity is said to be mobile.

volatile: readily forms a gas.

volatile fraction: the part of a liquid mixture that will vaporise readily under the conditions prevailing during the reaction. *See:* fraction, vapour.

water of crystallisation: the water molecules absorbed into the crystalline structure as a liquid changes to a solid. *Example:* hydrated copper(II) sulphate $CuSO_4 \cdot 5H_2O$. *See:* hydrate.

weak acid and **weak base**: an acid or base that has only partly dissociated (ionised) in water. Most organic acids are weak acids. *See:* organic acid.

weight: the gravitational force on a substance. *See:* mass.

X-rays: a form of very short wave radiation.

MASTER INDEX

0